CLASSIC

BRAINTEASERS

195 Puzzles to Keep You Sharp!

CLASSIC

BRAINTEASERS

195 Puzzles to Keep You Sharp!

By Karen C. Richards, Alan Stillson,
Bernardo Recamán Santos, et al.

STERLING INNOVATION
An imprint of Sterling Publishing Co., Inc.

New York / London
www.sterlingpublishing.com

STERLING and the distinctive Sterling logo are registered trademarks of
Sterling Publishing Co., Inc.

Library of Congress Cataloging-in-Publication Data Available

10 9 8 7 6 5

Published by Sterling Publishing Co., Inc.
387 Park Avenue South, New York, NY 10016
© 2002, 2008 by Sterling Publishing Co., Inc.

Material in this book previously appeared in *Mental Fitness Puzzles* © 1998 by
Matthew Kenneke, Daniel Hendrickson, Julie Hendrickson, and Kyle Hendrickson;
Nearly Impossible Brain Benders © 1998 by Tim Sole and Rod Marshall; *Mighty Mini
Mind Bogglers* © 1999 by Karen C. Richards; *Challenging Brainteasers* © 2000 by
Bernardo Recamán Santos; *One-Minute Brainteasers* © 2001 by Alan Stillson; all
published by Sterling Publishing Co., Inc.

Distributed in Canada by Sterling Publishing
c/o Canadian Manda Group, 165 Dufferin Street,
Toronto, Ontario, Canada M6K 3H6
Distributed in the United Kingdom by GMC Distribution Services
Castle Place, 166 High Street, Lewes, East Sussex, England BN7 1XU
Distributed in Australia by Capricorn Link (Australia) Pty. Ltd.
P.O. Box 704, Windsor, NSW 2756, Australia

Printed in China
All rights reserved

Sterling ISBN 978-1-4027-6011-2

For information about custom editions, special sales, premium and
corporate purchases, please contact Sterling Special Sales
Department at 800-805-5489 or specialsales@sterlingpublishing.com.

CLASSIC BRAINTEASERS

Contents

INTRODUCTION

With a trivia question, you either remember the fact or you do not. A brainteaser coaxes a little thought; it teases you into constructs or concepts of your own. We like to think of it as a kind of breezy mental gymnastics that's great fun!

Human beings have been solving, creating, and collecting games and puzzles for a long time. It could well be that the marks found on the Ishango bone discovered on the shores of Lake Edward in Central Africa, which date back some 11,000 years, were made by primitive man in an attempt to solve some kind of riddle, perhaps related to the lunar calendar.

What is certain is that early mathematicians in Babylonia and Egypt were avid puzzle creators and solvers. Many of the puzzles they dealt with were related to practical problems concerning their daily life, but often they were purely mental creations. Later, Greek mathematicians carried the tradition further. The solution to a puzzle set by Archimedes some 2,200 years ago about grazing cattle requires such huge numbers that it was only completed recently.

Puzzles and games continue to appeal to mathematicians and non-mathematicians alike. Once created, a good puzzle, like a good joke, travels widely, and takes a variety of forms. Often the same puzzle emerges in different places at about the same time. Like the creators of many of the best jokes, the creators of the finest puzzles and games remain anonymous. Once created, it is difficult to predict how puzzles will transform themselves as they move from one mind to another.

Most puzzles in this book can be solved within a few minutes. This allows you, the busy thinker, to control and time your mental workouts. Every puzzle can be solved independently. You can begin and end wherever and whenever you wish. When you're ready for more exercise, simply pick up where you left off.

Some puzzles may have alternate solutions that we didn't think of. Evaluate your results accordingly. Ready to rev up your mental motor? Here's your green light.

VISUAL TEASERS

Mind Boggler

Here's a quick brainteaser: What is special about the grid to the right— and what is missing from it?

Answer, page 207

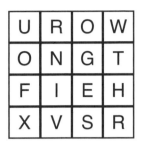

U	R	O	W
O	N	G	T
F	I	E	H
X	V	S	R

Tying the Knot

According to an ancient custom, if a woman throws five ropes out of a high window, and three or more of them land such that they will form knots when both ends are pulled, she will be married within the next year.

The ropes here show one woman's tosses. Should she expect a wedding this year?

Answer, page 213

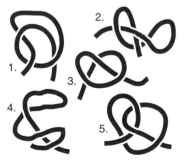

Technique-Color

Jo is making a stained-glass window, and she wants each adjacent piece of glass to be a different color. She wants to use just four colors: yellow, orange, purple, and red.

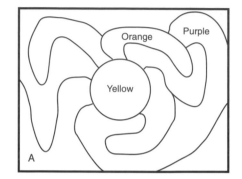

If the center circle is yellow, and two other pieces are colored as shown, what color does piece A need to be?
Answer, page 212

Animal Strength

If the first two tug of war contests shown here are ties, which group will win the third contest, or will it also be a draw?
Answer, page 203

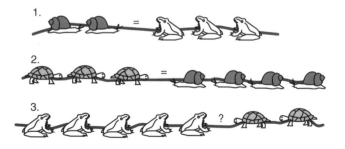

Theory of Relativity

At the Embee family reunion, your sister is talking to your grand-mother Mary, your cousin Bo, and your uncle Bill. Who are you?
Answer, page 213

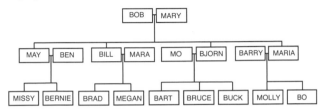

Paper Clip Flip

Most of the wire sculptures below were made from standard paper clips, by twisting them at existing bends.

Which of the shapes could not have been made by bending the original paper clip? *Answer, page 208*

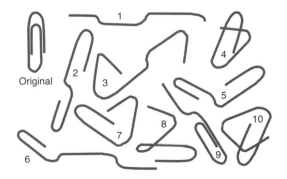

Block Party

The alphabet blocks below are of two different types, turned around in various positions. No letter appears on both types of block. The letters on the underside of the blocks spell out the answer to this riddle:

HOW DID BARBIE GET THROUGH THE PILE OF ALPHA-BET BLOCKS?

Can you do some mental tumbling and figure out the solution? *Answer, page 204*

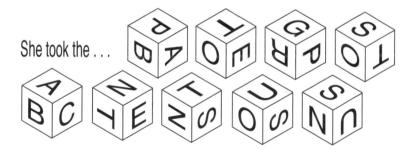

She took the . . .

Blind Alleys

On his birthday, Joe's friends blindfolded him and took him for a drive.

If they took two right turns, a left turn, and another left, and ended up at Wally World, where did they start? *Answer, page 204*

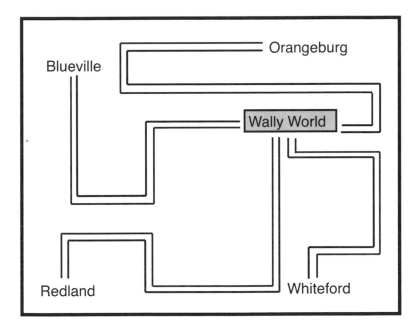

What's the Plan?

Which three-dimensional object at the bottom does the simple orthographic projection above it represent? *Answer, page 213*

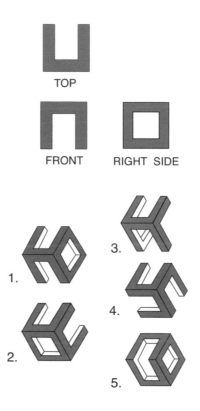

TOP

FRONT   RIGHT SIDE

1.

2.

3.

4.

5.

Three Hexes

Most of the shapes here can be made by combining three equal-sized hexagons. Which ones cannot? *Answer, page 213*

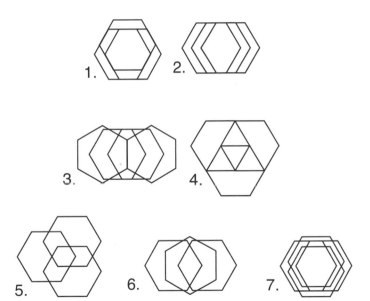

Ten Gold Coins

Ten gold coins are hidden under ten of the unlabeled hexagonal tiles in this floor. The numbers on the labeled tiles indicate how many coins are under tiles adjacent to that tile.

Can you locate the ten gold coins without looking under any of the wrong tiles? *Answer, page 212*

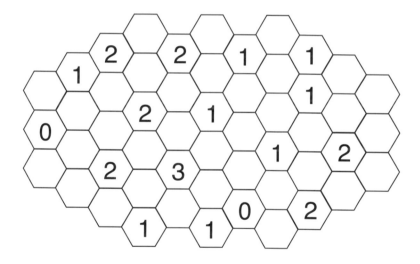

Mirror Images

Using only a square mirror and the jigsaw shape below, most of the figures below can be formed. Which figures are impossible? (Remember, parts of the new shapes are seen in the mirror.)

Answer, page 207

Winter Eyes

To make simple snowflakes, fold a square of paper into quarters, cut shapes, and unfold. Which folded snowflakes (1–7) will unfold to create snowflakes A, B, and C? *Answer, page 213*

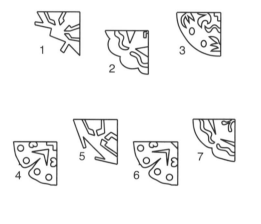

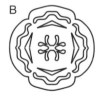

Fishing Lines

Today, eight people are trying to hook some trout on this part of the Lazy River.

Fishermen like to fish their own holes. To separate everyone, draw two straight lines across the map so that each fisher is on his or her own piece of river. Can you find a way for Mac to fish on his own piece of river? What about Bill? *Answer, page 205*

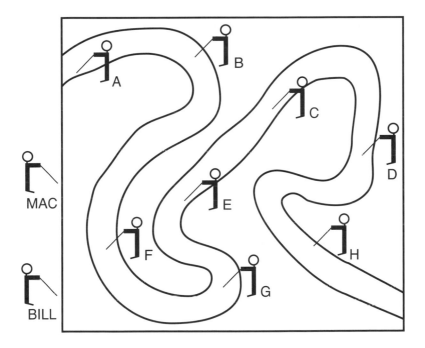

Black and White

In this game, you can see your friends' cards, but not your own. If there are four black cards and four white cards to choose from, can you deduce which cards you have by what the other players know? *Answer, page 203*

1.

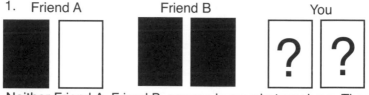

Neither Friend A, Friend B, nor you know what you have. Then, Friend A says she knows. What cards do you have?

2.

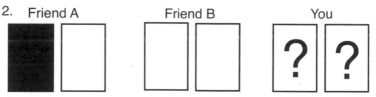

Neither Friend A, Friend B, nor you know what you have. Then, Friend A still doesn't know. What cards do you have?

Slice of Life

Your meatball pizza just came out of the oven and now you need to feed six hungry kids. These kids are picky, so they each want the same number of meatballs. They also each want the same size piece of pizza. How can you cut the pie to satisfy all six kids?

Answer, page 211

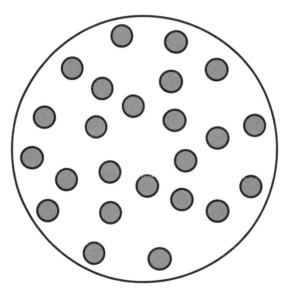

Game Plan

In these super tic-tac-toe games, the letters are entered from the top of the board, so that only the lowest empty box in each column can be played. If it's O's turn in game A and X's turn in game B, who should win each game? (Three X's or O's in a row wins.)
Answer, page 205

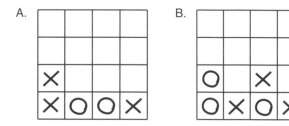

Shifting Gears

In each case, which way will gear C turn? *Answer, page 210*

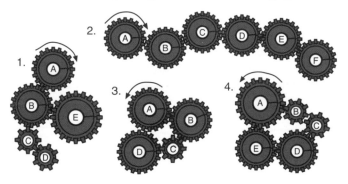

To the Letter

All of the eight shapes below are parts of the 26 letters shown above them, although they may have been enlarged and rotated. Figure out which letter each shape was taken from. The answers, in order, will spell a word. *Answer, page 213*

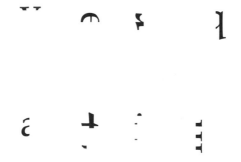

Irish Eyes

Can you find the four-leaf clover in this field? Good luck!
Answer, page 206

Key Rings

In each group below, if any one of the rings were picked up, would all of the other rings be lifted with it? *Answer, page 207*

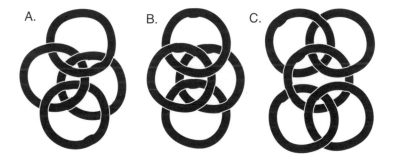

Jollos and Plotz

These are jollos:

These are plotz:

Which are jollos and which are plotz?

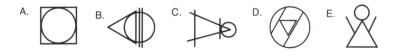

Answer, page 206

Paper Pinball

Begin at IN (10 points) and move along the lines to OUT (5 points), calculating as you go to get a high score. You may hit a bumper twice, but you may not trace over any part of your path. Our high score is 295. Can you beat it? *Answer, page 208*

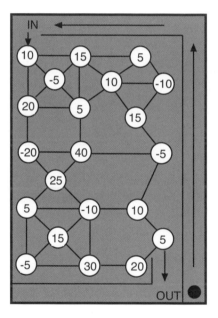

Jumper Cables

In gym class, the teacher told a group of kids each to grab a jump rope from a pile. Which two kids are holding the same rope?
Answer, page 206

Catch a Code

Use the Morse code key to help you solve the coded message. The message is written without breaks between letters. When decoded, the dots and dashes will answer this question:

What did the code inventor think when he had to repeat his message three times?

A	• —	N	— •
B	— • • •	O	— — —
C	— • — •	P	• — — •
D	— • •	Q	— — • —
E	•	R	• — •
F	• • — •	S	• • •
G	— — •	T	—
H	• • • •	U	• • —
I	• •	V	• • • —
J	• — — —	W	• — —
K	— • —	X	— • • —
L	• — • •	Y	— • — —
M	— —	Z	— — • •

MESSAGE: • • • • • • • • — • • • — • • —
• — • • — — — — — • — • • • •

Answer, page 204

Out of Shape

The original shape below can be flipped and rotated in many ways. Which of the figures is not a rotated version of the original shape? *Answer, page 208*

Original

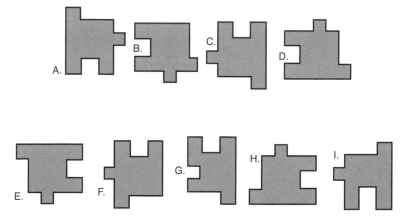

A. B. C. D.

E. F. G. H. I.

Domino Effect

Can you arrange the eight dominoes below to form a four-by-four square in which the number of pips in each row and column is the same? There is more than one answer. *Answer, page 204*

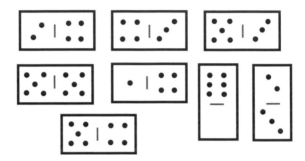

Talk for a Spell

Eight businesses in Centerville have phone numbers that spell out words appropriate for their services. Using the telephone number key, can you match each phone number to the business that uses it and name the word or words that each phone number stands for?

a. 356-9377	Travel agent
b. 967-5688	Coffee shop
c. 424-7288	Florist
d. 359-2929	Barber
e. 468-5282	Costume shop
f. 373-7787	Bank
g. 738-2273	Veterinarian
h. 728-3669	Health club

Answer, page 212

1	2 ABC	3 DEF
4 GHI	5 JKL	6 MNO
7 PRS	8 TUV	9 WXY

Beady Eyes

What number was added to the number on abacus A to get the total shown on abacus B? *Answer, page 203*

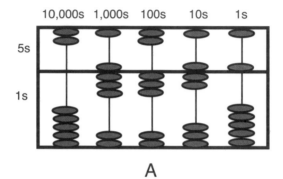

A

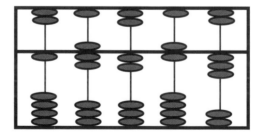

B

Symbol Maze

To solve this maze, you may move from one box to another only if they share a symbol. You will not use any symbol more than once. You may not move to any box that adjoins the box you are in (even diagonally). Start in the upper left corner and try to visit each box exactly once. *Answer, page 212*

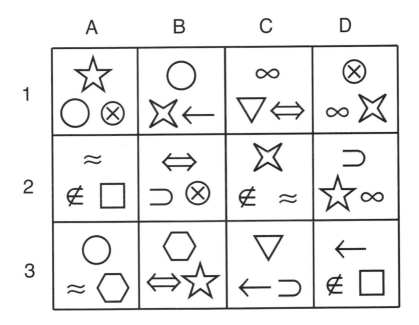

Receipt Deceit

The cash register printout at the Deuce hardware store isn't working very well. It is printing two sales on top of one another.

If Hank knows that one of his items cost $3.25, can you deduce the cost of his other purchases, his tax, and his total bill? Also, what were the amounts in the sale before his? *Answer, page 209*

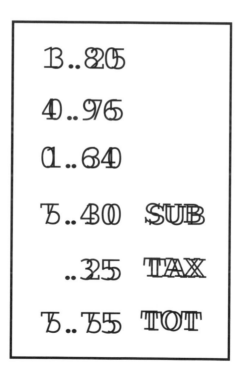

Starry Eyes

Can you find the one perfect, five-sided star in the field of shapes?
Answer, page 211

Pieces of Wisdom

If you can put these jigsaw pieces together mentally, you will find part of a quote from Ralph Waldo Emerson describing what it is to be successful. *Answer, page 209*

Draw by Numbers

Connect the points in the graph as directed. When you're done, you should see a familiar object.

Go from C10 to B10 to D13 to G14 to M14 to P13 to R10 to Q10 to P11 to N8 to N6 to P7 to Q7 to O4 to L5 to H5 to D1 to D2 to A5 to B6 to C5 to E5 to F9 to D11 to C10.

Then go from G9 to M9 to O12 to L13 to G13 to E12 to G9.
Answer, page 205

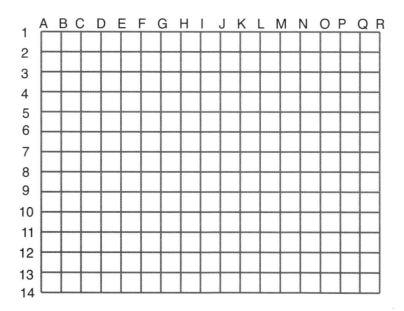

Unfolding Mystery

Two pieces of paper have been folded into fourths, and cut-outs have been made in them as shown (1 and 2). What will the unfolded pieces look like (a, b, c, d, e, or f)? *Answer, page 213*

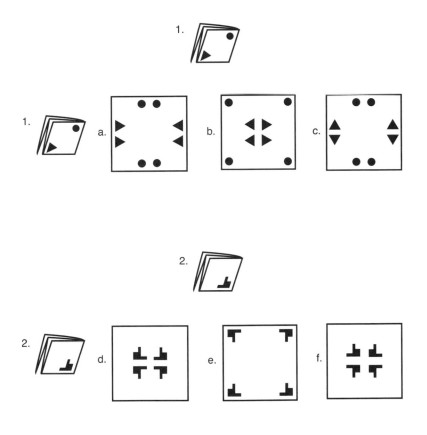

Making Faces

At an unusual costume party, every guest is wearing a mask showing the face of another one of the guests. The nametags match the masks. Can you name all of the people under the false faces?
Answer, page 207

Go for a Spin

In each case, can you mentally rotate the wheels so that six three-letter words are spelled from the outside ring to the center? Hint: All of the words in each grid have something in common.

Answer, page 206

Pretzel Logic

Which of the pretzel pieces below comes from a bag of Mrs. Saline pretzels and which ones must have come from a different brand? *Answer, page 209*

Mrs. Saline pretzel

1. 2. 3. 4.

5. 6. 7. 8. 9.

A Whale's Tale

Starting at the I in the upper left-hand corner, can you make knight's moves (see below) to jump to every square in the grid, without landing in any square twice, so that the letters you visit, in order, spell a phrase that tells you something about a blue whale's heart? *Answer, page 213*

I	N	E	S	B
T	P	T	I	N
U	N	E	E	E
E	I	T	I	M
S	T	R	M	A

Knight's move

1		
		2

Attention, Shoppers

Lusina spent exactly $29 at a garage sale. If only the items shown were for sale, and she paid the prices as they are marked, what did she buy? *Answer, page 203*

ATLAS $3   HAT $11   PICTURE $4

LAMP $7   MAILBOX $5   IRON $8

Number Lines

Can you draw the straight line that passes through the highest number total for each box below? *Answer, page 208*

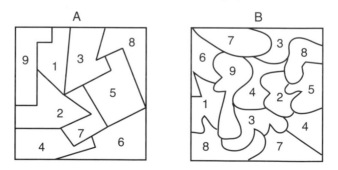

A   B

Ready to Roll

One of the dice below is not a standard die. Which one is the fake?
Answer, page 209

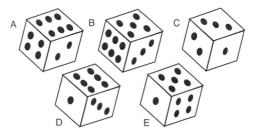

Circular Notions

The circles below are hiding two interesting words. To find the words, start at the top letter in each case, and count clockwise a number of spaces (the number is for you to determine) to the next letter. Then, keep counting the same number of spaces and landing on a new letter until all the letters are used. *Answer, page 204*

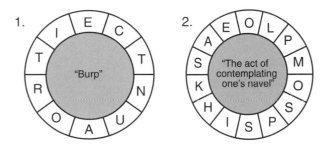

Sketch Pad

Al came across these two Etch A Sketch drawings in a toy store. Can you figure out how someone drew each shape using one continuous line, not retracing any part of either figure? *Answer, page 210*

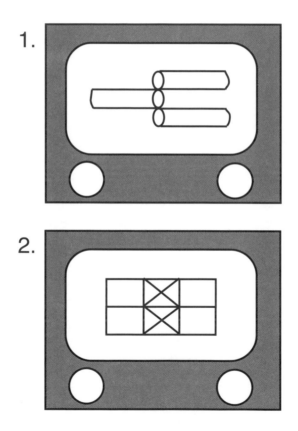

Picture This

When overlapped, the lines on the two squares below will form a picture. Can you figure out which way to rotate the squares and what appears in the combined image? The squares do not need to be flipped over, and they should be rotated in 90° increments.

Answer, page 209

A.

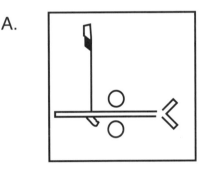

B.

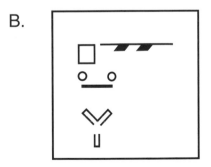

Gone to Pieces

Only 10 pieces remain in your animal cracker box, below. What animals were they? *Answer, page 206*

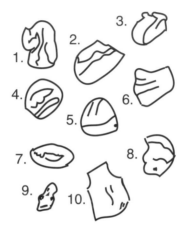

LED Astray

The LED display on Art's calculator is malfunctioning. Only the top halves of the characters are showing. What equation is displayed below?

If only the bottom halves of the display are showing, what are the two possibilities for the equation? *Answer, page 207*

LATERAL THINKING

LATERAL THINKING

Lateral thinking is a process of freeing your mind of preconceptions and allowing yourself to approach problems in an unconventional way.

The clues given for the puzzle problems in this section are especially helpful. Although responses are confined to either "Yes," "No," or "Irrelevant," they allow you to validate guesses without peeking at the answer. We realize that some of the puzzles may have more than one plausible answer, but suggest that the solver be encouraged to determine the solution provided.

A Fire Escape

Nicole awakes to the smell of smoke. Although she realizes the danger in her situation, she makes no attempt to leave the building where she has been sleeping. Why?

Answer, page 219

Clues:

Q: Was Nicole physically capable of walking on her own?
A: Yes

Q: Was the fire blocking Nicole's path of escape?

A: No

Q: Was Nicole sleeping in her own home?

A: No

Q: Could Nicole have left the building if the fire had not occurred?

A: No

Brainbender #1

What word, expression, or name is depicted below?

Answer, page 231

The Unsuccessful Suicide

Feeling suicidal, a man tries to kill himself by jumping off a high-rise building. He miraculously survives the fall. Why don't the police charge him with attempted suicide?

Answer, page 230

Clues:

Q: Was the man really trying to commit suicide?

A: Yes

Q: If he had jumped from the building the day before, would he have been arrested?

A: Yes

Q: Did the police think the man was trying to commit suicide?

A: No

Q: Were the police at the scene solely for the purpose of saving his life?

A: No

Brainbender #2

What word, expression, or name is depicted below?
Answer, page 231

Theft in a Pub

J.P. visits his favorite local pub. While coming back from the restroom he sees a stranger take his wallet from his jacket, which he had left draped over his chair. J.P. watches the thief spend the money. Can you explain this passive response?

Answer, page 229

Clues:

Q: Was the pub known for having a shady reputation?
A: Yes

Q: Did J.P. want the thief to steal the money?
A: Yes

Q: Was J.P. a criminal himself?
A: Yes

Q: Did J.P. learn something from watching the thief spend the money?
A: Yes

To Tell a Mockingbird

Christopher learns about a terrible crime that has been committed by John and Bob. He has known both of these men for many years and cares for them equally. Why, then, does he only report Bob to the authorities and not John?

Answer, page 230

Clues:

Q: Did Christopher have something to gain by turning in only John?

A: No

Q: If John had been a total stranger, would Christopher have turned him in?

A: No

Q: Did Christopher learn of Bob's illegal activities in a different setting than he did John's?

A: Yes

Brainbender #3

What word, expression, or name is depicted below?
Answer, page 231

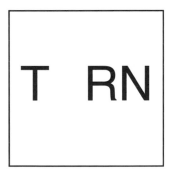

More Than He Bargained For

One day, while he is window shopping, Bert is suddenly aware that his retirement nest egg is gone. Can you explain how Bert came to this realization?

Answer, page 223

Clue:

Q: Is there something that Bert sees which causes this realization?
A: Yes

Q: Was Bert's retirement nest egg stored in a safe place?
A: No

Q: If Bert was window shopping in the same store a minute earlier or later, would he have come to the same conclusion?
A: No

Brainbender #4

What word, expression, or name is depicted below?
Answer, page 230

The Frustrated Futures Trader

Every day, on his drive to work in downtown Manhattan from his home in New Jersey, Joe is frustrated by his lack of foresight. Why?
Answer, page 220

Clues:

Q: Is the location of Joe's home important?

A: Yes

Q: Does Joe's frustration occur at a specific place and/or time each day?

A: Yes

Q: Is there something unusual about Joe's car?

A: Yes

Brainbender #5

What word, expression, or name is depicted below?
Answer, page 230

An Untimely Death

Cal loves his pet, Roscoe, very much. In fact, he even brings Roscoe to work with him every day. After returning from lunch one day, Cal and his co-workers were very alarmed to find Roscoe dead. Can you explain the panic which followed their discovery? *Answer, page 230*

Clues:

Q: Is it important to know what type of animal Roscoe was?
A: Yes

Q: Would it help to determine Cal's occupation?
A: Yes

Q: Did Cal and his co-workers fear that they might die from the same cause as Roscoe?
A: Yes

The Long Road Ahead

Bubba sets out on a hazardous journey. Although his destination is in sight the entire time, he has to travel 400 miles in order to reach his destination. Can you explain the circumstances surrounding this event? *Answer, page 222*

Clues:

Q: Could Bubba have taken a shortcut to reach his destination?

A: No

Q: Could Bubba have driven 399 miles and walked the remaining mile to reach his goal?

A: No

Q: Did other people undertake the same journey at the same time?

A: Yes

Brainbender #6

What word, expression, or name is depicted below?
Answer, page 227

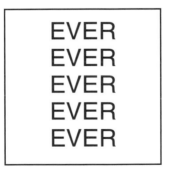

The Prison Break

Jim develops an elaborate plan to escape from prison. After successfully escaping, Jim makes a mocking phone call to the prison authorities. He reveals that he is only a few miles away at a local tavern frequented by many off-duty prison guards. The authorities are dismayed by this news, yet make no attempt to take him back into custody. Can you explain their unusual reaction?
Answer, page 226

Clues:

Q: Was Jim ever convicted of a crime?
A: No

Q: Was Jim ever accused of committing a crime?
A: No

Q: Did Jim know that he wouldn't be taken back into custody?
A: Yes

Wood That I Could

Tom is stranded on a island. Although he has firewood and matches, he spends several nights shivering and cold. On the tenth night it begins to rain and Tom decides to light a fire. What's going on here? *Answer, page 232*

Clues:

Q: Did Tom light the fire to keep warm?

A: No

Q: Would Tom have lit the fire if it wasn't raining?

A: Yes

Q: Does the rain have any significance as to why Tom lit the fire?

A: No

Q: Does Tom have only a limited amount of firewood?

A: Yes

Brainbender #7

What word, expression, or name is depicted below?

Answer, page 230

BEND
DRAW
DRAW
DRAW

A Shooting at Midnight

A man walks into his backyard in the middle of the night and fires a gun. Due to his strange behavior he never sees another sunrise. (No, he didn't kill himself!) Can you explain this odd occurrence? *Answer, page 228*

Clues:

Q: Was the man trying to hit something?
A: Yes

Q: Was the man injured in any way?
A: No

Q: Did the man want to see the sunrise?
A: No

Q: Was the intended target important?
A: Yes

Execution at Dawn

After a short court-martial, General Gordo selects seven of his best marksmen to serve on a firing squad. They fire on the condemned man at point-blank range, yet only six bullets are found in his body. Why? *Answer, page 218*

Clues:

Q: Were all seven marksmen aiming at the same man?

A: Yes

Q: Were all seven rifles in good working order?

A: Yes

Q: After examining the body, were they surprised to find only six bullets in the man's body?

A: No

Brainbender #8

What word, expression, or name is depicted below?
Answer, page 229

The Leaky Boat

Al is a well-known boat builder. He spends nearly a year hand-crafting a boat from the finest timber available. When he finally launches his boat it sinks within a few minutes. Satisfied, he returns home. Can you explain the man's reaction?

Answer, page 221

Clues:

Q: Did Al attempt to keep the boat from sinking?
A: No

Q: Was this an unusual occurrence?
A: No

Q: Did Al have a reason for leaving the boat underwater?
A: Yes

Q: Was the sinking beneficial to the boat in some way?
A: Yes

Wonder Woman

A woman is at work. She is asked to move a two-ton piece of equipment. Although no one assists her and there are no mechanical aids available, she easily completes the task. How does she comply with this seemingly impossible request?

Answer, page 231

Clues:

Q: Is there anything physically unusual about the woman that permits her to perform this feat?

A: No

Q: Are there any special conditions that allowed her to accomplish this task?

A: Yes

Q: Is the woman's occupation important?

A: Yes

Brainbender #9

What word, expression, or name is depicted below?
Answer, page 228

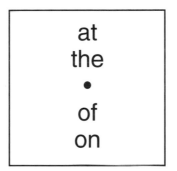

By the Time I Get to Phoenix

One day Nick boasted to his friend, Frank, that he had once driven an automobile from coast to coast in less than twenty-four hours. Naturally, Frank realizes that Nick has finally stretched the truth to the breaking point. Frank offers his boastful buddy five thousand dollars if Nick can duplicate his miraculous driving feat. Although it pained him greatly to do so, Frank conceded defeat as soon as Nick explained how it could be done. What was Nick's explanation?
Answer, page 216

Clues:

Q: Did Nick plan to make this drive in another country?
A: No

Q: Could Nick have actually performed this feat if Frank had asked him to?
A: Yes

Q: Could the average person have accomplished this task?
A: Yes

Dead Men Tell No Tales

A search party was looking for a man. They finally found him lying in a field covered in blood. Later that day, the coroner revealed that the man had been shot twice. Without any other physical evidence, the police quickly arrested the murderer. How were the police able to ascertain the identity of the criminal?
Answer, page 217

Clues:

Q: Was anyone in the search party aware of who the criminal was before arriving at the crime scene?

A: No

Q: Did the murderer turn himself in?

A: No

Q: Was the time of death important to the solving of the crime?

A: Yes

Brainbender #10

What word, expression, or name is depicted below?
Answer, page 226

Out of Bounds

In November of 1952 a momentous football game took place between two fierce rivals. With two minutes to go in the fourth quarter, a field goal was kicked to tie the score at 13–13. Despite the loud protests of the players and spectators, the game was declared a draw, and it was not completed or replayed. Why would the game officials make such a dissatisfying and unpopular ruling? *Answer, page 224*

Clues:

Q: Did the fans realize what the problem was?
A: Yes

Q: Did they have all of the equipment necessary to play the game after the field goal was kicked?
A: No

Q: Does it matter where the game was being played?
A: Yes

Swimming with the Fishes

A man was fishing on a large lake when he suddenly fell in. Although the man was an accomplished swimmer and was only a few yards away from shore, he eventually drowned. Why did this happen? *Answer, page 229*

Clues:

Q: Did something prevent him from reaching shore?

A: Yes

Q: Did the man fall into the lake from a boat?

A: No

Q: Does it matter what type of fishing he was doing?

A: Yes

Brainbender #11

What word, expression, or name is depicted below?

Answer, page 226

STEP

PETS

PETS

Sweet Success

Charlotte picks up a teaspoon of sugar using only one finger. How?
Answer, page 217

Clues:

Q: Did Charlotte use any tools or aids to help her do this?
A: No

Q: Was the sugar held within a container?
A: No

Q: Was the sugar in powder form?
A: No

Brainbender #12

What word, expression, or name is depicted below?
Answer, page 225

The Runaway

Alex is at a sporting event, minding his own business and, in fact, in deep concentration. Suddenly, right in front of him, a   man appears, takes something from him, and quickly runs off. Instead of trying to catch the man and retrieve the item, Alex simply stands passively and watches as he runs away. Why?

Answer, page 227

Clues:

Q: Was Alex afraid to chase the man?
A: No

Q: Is the item that the man took significant?
A: Yes

Q: Did Alex know the man who took the object away from him?
A: Yes

Shortchanged

Minnie receives a sure-fire gambling tip that would put her on Easy Street. She has several dollars' worth of change in her pocket and finds a working pay phone to call her bookie. Why, then, does she lose out on her one and only chance at making the "big score"?

Answer, page 228

Clues:

Q: Was her bookie's phone busy?
A: No

Q: Did anyone stop Minnie from making the phone call?
A: No

Q: Did Minnie ever make a phone call?
A: No

Money Troubles

A man is charged with a crime and placed in jail. His bond is set at one hundred thousand dollars. Although he desperately wants to leave and could easily get the money, he decides to remain in jail. Why? *Answer, page 222*

Clues:

Q: Would the man have feared for his life if he had left the jail?
A: No

Q: If his bail had been posted by someone else, would he leave?
A: Yes

Q: Does the type of crime he was charged with have any relevance?
A: Yes

Q: Was the man guilty of the crime with which he had been charged?
A: Yes

Photo Finished

Ben is accused of murder. He claimed that at the time the murder had taken place, he was on vacation in the South Pacific. To back up his alibi he provided the police with videotapes of his week-long vacation. Why, then, was he eventually convicted of the crime?

Answer, page 225

Clues:

Q: Did the videotape tip the police off?
A: Yes

Q: Were the tapes filmed in the South Pacific?
A: Yes

Q: If Ben had filmed only during the day, would he have been caught?
A: No

Keep on Truckin'

Lewis attends the International Convention of Truckers. While in the noisy convention hall he sees a group of men on the far side of the room. He does not recognize any of them. Without hearing them speak or seeing anything distinctive about their wardrobe, Lewis announces to his colleagues: "There's the group from Australia. I think I'll go over and introduce myself." How did he come to his rapid and accurate conclusion?

Answer, page 221

Clues:

Q: Did Lewis see something that led him to this conclusion?
A: Yes

Q: Is there something about their physical appearance that gave Lewis a clue to their origin?
A: Yes

Q: Is it important that they drive on the left-hand side of the road in Australia?
A: Yes

Brainbender #13

What word, expression, or name is depicted below?
Answer, page 224

Mr. Gray's Anatomy

Mr. Gray's life was going perfectly. He was healthy, successful, and had a beautiful family. Therefore his parents were shocked when he made a very strange request. Mr. Gray asked that his head be cut off. Why did he make this bizarre request?

Answer, page 224

Clues:

Q: Did Mr. Gray simply want to commit suicide?

A: No

Q: Would it have been legal for Mr. Gray's parents to comply with his request?

A: Yes

Q: Might Mr. Gray have made the same request if it had been 1892 instead of 1992?

A: No

Potted Plants

When Fred decided to grow a large quantity of marijuana on his remote farm, he thought he had the perfect plan. He would grow the plants in a large barn using artificial lights. No one ever visited him and he was the only person involved in the operation. So it was a great surprise when, months later, Fred was arrested and his illicit crop seized. Fred could not figure out what had caused his scheme to unravel. Can you?

Answer, page 226

Clues:

Q: Was Fred detected through a type of surveillance?
A: No

Q: Did Fred's day-to-day activities appear suspicious?
A: No

Q: Was there something Fred needed to obtain which caused him to come under suspicion?
A: Yes

Q: Could Fred have purchased this at a regular store?
A: No

Brainbender #14

What word, expression, or name is depicted below?
Answer, page 224

The Sky Diver

Pierre went skydiving near his home in Dallas, Texas. As a result, Pierre saved his brother's life. Strangely though, his brother lived in Boston and hadn't seen or spoken to his brother Pierre for a great many years. How could this miracle have taken place?

Answer, page 229

Clues:

Q: Did Pierre discover something which was a help to his brother?

A: No

Q: If Pierre had stayed home that day, could he have saved his brother's life?

A: No

Q: Did Pierre communicate some information to his brother which saved his brother's life?

A: No

Eyes on the Prize

The Stardust Lounge was holding its annual raffle. First prize was $1,000 dollars in cash. Hopeful participants wrote their names on slips of paper which were then placed in a large bowl. When Alexander Turnbull's name was announced as the winner, he was both surprised and excited, yet he did not claim the money. Why not?

Answer, page 219

Clues:

Q: Was Alexander afraid to claim the prize?
A: No

Q: Did he fill out an entry form?
A: No

Q: Did someone else fill his name in on the form?
A: Yes

The Alaskan Dream

Scott is an expert outdoorsman, pursuing his dream by living alone in the remote Alaskan wilderness. Scott has everything he needs, and would prefer to remain a recluse, yet he will have to leave his home in four years. Why?

Answer, page 215

Clues:

Q: Was something going to happen that would destroy Scott's home?
A: No

Q: Did Scott need to return to civilization in order to buy food or clothing?
A: No

Q: Would Scott have been in danger if he ignored the four-year deadline?
A: Yes

A Bridge to Fear

On her way to work one blustery winter day, Patty slipped and fell over the railing of the world's highest suspension bridge. She was wearing only her regular office attire, yet she was not harmed in any way. How could that be?

Answer, page 216

Clues:

Q: Is the type of work Patty did relevant?
A: No

Q: Did something cushion the impact of Patty's fall from the bridge?
A: No

Q: Could the average person have survived this fall?
A: Yes

Q: Does it matter where Patty was located on the bridge when she fell?
A: Yes

Petty Cash

When Pauline's house was burglarized, five dollars were taken from a dresser drawer. Nothing else was stolen or damaged. After filing a claim with her insurance company, Pauline was paid one thousand dollars for her loss. What was the reasoning behind this settlement?

Answer, page 225

Clues:

Q: Did Pauline falsify the claim she made to her insurance company?

A: No

Q: Was there anything unusual about the stolen money?

A: Yes

Brainbender #15

What word, expression, or name is depicted below?
Answer, page 223

Feast or Famine

After months of subsisting on a starvation diet, Paul finally obtained some decent food. Why, then, did he pass up this opportunity to enjoy a perfectly good meal?
Answer, page 219

Clues:

Q: Was Paul allergic to the food?

A: No

Q: Was Paul on a hunger strike before he received the food?

A: No

Q: Does it matter that he was already malnourished to begin with?

A: Yes

An Axe to Grind

When Jerry, a lumberjack known for exaggeration, boasted of cutting down a one-hundred-year-old maple tree in ten seconds using only a small axe, his friend Mac had had enough. He challenged Jerry to prove his incredible claim. How did the brawny braggart succeed? *Answer, page 215*

Clues:

Q: Was the tree healthy at the time Jerry cut it down?

A: Yes

Q: Was there something special about Jerry?

A: No

Q: Would this tree supply a lot of firewood?

A: No

The Root of the Problem

Mr. Finkel was an avid gardener who was very proud of his landscaping and horticultural skills. Unfortunately, Mr. Finkel's hobby caused the death of a neighbor after he planted a tree in his backyard. How could his gentle pastime have turned deadly?

Answer, page 227

Clues:

Q: Did the tree obstruct or hinder anyone's view?

A: No

Q: If Mr. Finkel had planted the same tree in a different spot in his yard, would the outcome have been the same?

A: No

Q: If Mr. Finkel had planted the tree a day later or a day earlier, would he have been responsible for his neighbor's death?

A: No

The Sky's the Limit

Henry, a poor but lucky fisherman, finds a treasure map that promises great wealth beyond his wildest dreams. He ultimately retrieves the loot which lay buried on an island barely a day's sail from his home. Why did Henry wait three months to retrieve the loot?

Answer, page 229

Clues:

Q: Was Henry able to travel when he first found the map?

A: Yes

Q: If someone else had discovered the map, would they also have waited?

A: Yes

Q: Was there something unusual about the map?

A: Yes

Brainbender #16

What word, expression, or name is depicted below?

Answer, page 223

The Discouraging Discovery

During the aftermath of a violent storm, Vern is pleased to find that his house has come through unscathed. Later that day, Vern discovers that he has suffered a large loss in the value of his property. What led Vern to this unfortunate conclusion?

Answer, page 217

Clues:

Q: Did Vern discover that his house was not worth as much as he had thought?

A: Yes

Q: Did the storm uncover or disturb something that led Vern to discover the loss?

A: Yes

Q: Was storm damage elsewhere on the property the cause of the loss of value?

A: No

Q: Is the age of Vern's house significant?

A: Yes

The Expert Pilot

A man is flying a plane. When the engine begins to stall, the pilot immediately switches to his reserve fuel tank. Later in the flight, the landing gear warning light comes on, yet the pilot is not concerned with this new, potentially lethal problem. Why not?

Answer, page 218

Clues:

Q: Is the plane capable of landing without using landing gear?
A: No

Q: Does he plan to parachute out of the plane?
A: No

Q: Is the man a military pilot?
A: Yes

Q: Did this occur during wartime?
A: Yes

Brainbender #17

What word, expression, or name is depicted below?
Answer, page 223

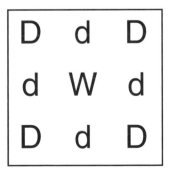

What's It All About?

Mack goes on an eating binge for several days, which ends up costing him two million dollars. How?
Answer, page 231

Clues:

Q: Did Mack spend all or a good part of this money while on his eating binge?

A: No

Q: If Mack had started his binge one month later, would it still have cost him the money?

A: No

Q: Is it important that Mack had gained a lot of weight?

A: Yes

Brainbender #18

What word, expression, or name is depicted below?
Answer, page 222

The Mysterious Motorist

Every so often, Jennifer pulls off to the side of the road and opens the trunk of her car. She doesn't get anything out of the trunk or put anything into it. Can you give a reason for this seemingly strange activity? *Answer, page 224*

Clues:

Q: Was Jennifer having car trouble?

A: No

Q: Does Jennifer do this on a regular basis?

A: Yes

Q: Could any of the passing motorists tell why Jennifer had opened the trunk?

A: Yes

Q: Was she working when this occurred?

A: Yes

A Sense of Direction

On the first day of a business trip to Japan, B.J. arrives at a large office building. She had never been there before, and could not read any of the signs. Without seeing or talking with anyone, she quickly makes her way through a labyrinth of hallways to arrive at her destination. How? *Answer, page 227*

Clues:

Q: Were there any other visual clues that helped B.J. find her destination?

A: No

Q: Did B.J. hear something that helped her find her way?

A: No

Q: Could B.J. have done this in any other building?

A: No

Moving Day

Herb gets a job in a new city. On the day of his move, Herb causes a traffic jam without ever leaving his home. How does Herb create such a monumental disturbance?

Answer, page 223

Clues:

Q: If Herb had moved on another day, would he still have caused a traffic jam?

A: Yes

Q: Did Herb have to pack anything prior to moving?

A: No

Q: Did Herb live in a traditional type of home?

A: No

I Bid Thee Farewell

Dee places an ad soliciting bids for the construction of a new office building. In response, she receives two bids. Without opening either, she immediately throws one away. Why did she make such a rash decision? *Answer, page 220*

Clues:

Q: Did Dee know beforehand that the bid would be unacceptable?

A: No

Q: If the bid had been received via fax machine, would it have been considered?

A: Yes

Q: Is the type of business that Dee works for important?

A: Yes

Shed Some Light

A hermit inherits a large amount of money and has a new house built. Although he enjoys his new home immensely, he only uses the lights during the day. Why does he do this?

Answer, page 228

Clues:

Q: Is he saving money?

A: No

Q: Is he trying to hide for some reason?

A: No

Q: Does he have electricity available at all times?

A: No

Brainbender #19

What word, expression, or name is depicted below?
Answer, page 222

A Hunting Accident

Mick often went hunting in the extensive marshlands which surrounded the local airport. One day, a plane was forced to make a crash landing. Although Mick never fired his rifle, or any other weapon, his hunting trip was directly responsible for the tragedy. How did Mick's hunting trip turn deadly?

Answer, page 220

Clues:

Q: Is this a regular-size plane, not a model or toy?
A: Yes

Q: Does Mick use an unusual hunting method?
A: Yes

Q: Did he cause something to collide with the plane?
A: Yes

Q: If the plane had been propeller driven, would it have crashed?
A: No

Down on the Farm

Two farmers, Jedro and Jason, have farms that are adjacent to each other. They both plant the same crop and use identical techniques. Furthermore, both of the farms measure ten miles long by ten miles wide. Why, then, is Jedro able to produce ten percent more grain than Jason every year?

Answer, page 218

Clues:

Q: Did both farmers have access to the same water supply?

A: Yes

Q: Could a passerby determine why Jedro's farm produces more grain each year?

A: Yes

Q: Had the two farmers exchanged properties, would Jedro continue to produce more grain than Jason?

A: No

Long Time No See

Kathy receives a call from an old friend and roommate on the phone. She has known this person intimately for years, yet Kathy does not recognize her friend's voice. How can this be?
Answer, page 222

Clues:

Q: Did something happen to her friend's voice?

A: No

Q: Did Kathy have any physical or mental disabilities, such as deafness or amnesia?

A: No

Q: Had they ever spoken to each other before?

A: No

Whose Vault Is It?

A burglar is stealing two bars of gold, each so heavy he cannot lift it above his waist. On his way out of the vault, he suddenly sees a security camera ahead. Thinking quickly, he disguises himself without putting down the gold bars. How?

Answer, page 231

Clues:

Q: Was he wearing anything on his head?

A: No

Q: Did the criminal cover his face with something?

A: Yes

Q: Did he cover his face with something burglars typically use while robbing banks?

A: No

Brainbender #20

What word, expression, or name is depicted below?
Answer, page 215

On the Boardwalk

Patrick has a regular delivery route along the Myrtle Beach board-walk. Each day he makes his deliveries using a handcart and returns to his shop at the north end of the boardwalk. Although he is not physically tired, Patrick always finds that the return trip, with his cart now empty, is more difficult. Why?

Answer, page 224

Clues:

Q: Is the boardwalk completely flat?
A: Yes

Q: Is Patrick carrying anything back with him on his return trip?
A: No

Q: Is the type of merchandise important?
A: Yes

Q: Does the merchandise assist him in moving the cart?
A: Yes

The Secret Meeting

A man and a woman meet at their regular time and place. They have an intimate conversation together, yet neither one can describe the other to their friends. Why?

Answer, page 227

Clues:

Q: Is the man's profession relevant?

A: Yes

Q: Does the man speak intimately with other people on a regular basis?

A: Yes

Q: Is the exact location of their meetings important?

A: Yes

Brainbender #21

What word, expression, or name is depicted below?
Answer, page 216

Temporary Housing

Jake builds a house, and although anyone would be satisfied with the construction, he knows he'll have to re-build it in fifteen years. Why? *Answer, page 229*

Clues:

Q: Did Jake use materials that would last only 15 years?

A: No

Q: Did Jake build a traditional house?

A: No

Brainbender #22

What word, expression, or name is depicted below?
Answer, page 217

A Customs Conundrum

Eric spends his vacation in the Swiss Alps. Unfortunately, he ends up spending the greater part of his visit in the hospital, after having taken a nasty spill while skiing. On his return trip home to the U.S., the authorities do not ask him to show his passport. Why not?
Answer, page 217

Clues:

Q: Was Eric hiding from the Customs authorities?

A: No

Q: Was Eric an important official who was exempt from this procedure?

A: No

Q: Did the type of transportation Eric was using matter?

A: No

Q: Did the customs officials check the passports of any of the passengers?

A: Yes

The Yard Sale

After buying a new oven, Gerald sold his old one to a stranger. Although the stranger offered to pay cash, Gerald, nonetheless, had a very good reason for insisting that the transaction take place at a bank. Rather than be offended, the stranger clearly understood the reason for this unusual request. Why did Gerald make this demand?
Answer, page 232

Clues:

Q: Did Gerald know how to count?

A: Yes

Q: Did the man have the correct currency?

A: Yes

Q: Would he have insisted on going to the bank, had he sold the oven to a friend?

A: No

The Master Mechanic

Gary, a highly skilled auto mechanic, climbed under the chassis of Shawn's midnight-blue Pontiac GTO. Ten minutes later he climbed out from under the car. Gary did not inspect or repair the automobile, nor did he offer any professional advice to the car's owner. In fact, Shawn knew full well that Gary had never even touched the vehicle. Immediately afterwards, and as a result of what had just occurred, Shawn unhesitatingly paid Gary five hundred dollars. Why would he do this?

Answer, page 222

Clues:

Q: Did Shawn expect Gary to do any work on the car?

A: No

Q: Is Gary's occupation important?

A: No

Q: Would it help to know where Shawn's car was parked at the time Gary climbed under it?

A: Yes

The King's Test

An eccentric king wanted to find the smartest person in his kingdom. He had one bucket of milk and another bucket of water, both filled to the rim. He then said, "Whoever can mix these together to form a 50/50 mixture without using anything other than these two buckets will receive a thousand gold coins." How did one man finally succeed?

Answer, page 221

Clues:

Q: Does the man pour the milk or water at any time?

A: No

Q: Does the man accomplish this task quickly?

A: No

Q: Could milk and vodka, for example, be used for the test?

A: No

Hard of Darkness

Tim and Ralph were the best of friends. They were also very competitive. Over the years, Tim and Ralph have met each and every challenge, both mental and physical, posed by the other. One day, Tim succeeds in posing a challenge that Ralph cannot possibly meet. What is the challenge? *Answer, page 220*

Clues:

Q: Are Tim and Ralph of the same sex?

A: Yes

Q: Did the challenge require some specific knowledge that Ralph could not possibly have possessed?

A: No

Q: Could the average man win the bet?

A: Yes

Q: If you looked at the two friends, would you know why Ralph was unable to meet the challenge?

A: Yes

Crustacean Vacation

After being away on business for a week, Milton checked with his son to see how their crabbing business had prospered during his absence. When his son reported that things had slacked off all week, the father was disappointed, yet he trusted his son's response. The next day, as they prepared to launch their boat,

Milton began scolding his son for lying. How did he know his son had deceived him? *Answer, page 216*

Clues:

Q: Did Milton check with someone else to see if his son was lying?

A: No

Q: Would it help to know where the crab boat had been stored?

A: Yes

Q: Did Milton have reason to believe the boat had not been used during his absence?

A: Yes

Brainbender #23

What word, expression, or name is depicted below?
Answer, page 218

Attorney Client Privilege

Sam is talking to his lawyer in jail. They are very upset because the judge has refused to grant bail. Oddly enough, at the end of the conversation Sam is allowed to leave the jail. Why?

Answer, page 215

Clues:

Q: Is it important why Sam was in jail?

A: Yes

Q: Did Sam's lawyer provide Sam with any legal assistance that day?

A: No

Q: Could Sam have been able to get out of jail if his lawyer had *not* been there?

A: Yes

Harry the Homeowner

Harry goes out and buys a new house. One day he returns home to find that all of the furniture in the house has been completely rearranged. Strangely, Harry is not in the least bit surprised or irritated, even though he didn't ask anyone to do this. Why?

Answer, page 220

Clues:

Q: Does it matter why Harry bought the house?

A: Yes

Q: Did Harry know who had moved the furniture?

A: Yes

Q: Could anyone have lived in this house?

A: No

The Big Game

One of the most prominent citizens of Chicago once offered highly prized football tickets to forty people whom he despised. Can you explain his unusual generosity?

Answer, page 215

Clues:

Q: Was the man trying to get rid of tickets?

A: No

Q: Was the game upcoming and scheduled for a convenient time and place?

A: Yes

Q: Did the people who were offered the tickets actually get to use them to go to the game?

A: No

Q: Did the man have the tickets available to give away?

A: No

First Edition

Mr. Jones drives a hundred miles to the nearest bookstore. He pays twenty dollars of his hard-earned money to purchase a first edition of a new book. After many hours of reading, he concludes that the book is poorly written, boring, and inaccurate. Rather than be upset, Mr. Jones is instead greatly pleased with his purchase. Why would this be? *Answer, page 219*

Clues:

Q: If Mr. Jones had found it accurate and interesting, would he be upset?

A: Yes

Q: Does Mr. Jones have special knowledge of the book's subject matter?

A: Yes

Q: Does Mr. Jones have a financial interest in the book's success or failure?

A: Yes

A Reverting Development

An artist, working in his private studio, had just finished a new creation, so he decided to take a break and visit an old friend. During his visit a violent storm erupted. The artist soon realized that his work of art would be ruined. How did he know?
Answer, page 226

Clues:

Q: If he had been at home, could he have prevented the work of art from being ruined?

A: No

Q: Is it important to know what type of artist he was?

A: Yes

Q: Does it matter what material the artist was using?

A: Yes

Brainbender #24

What word, expression, or name is depicted below?
Answer, page 219

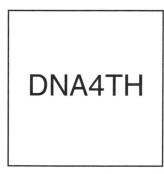

Monumental Achievement

A man makes his way to the top of a hundred-foot-high monument in the center of a small town. He then jumps off the monument without the aid of a parachute, glider, or other such device. He is not harmed in any way. How did he manage to do this?

Answer, page 223

Clues:

Q: Was there something special about the man which enabled him to perform this feat?

A: No

Q: Did the man fear being injured as he leaped off the monument?

A: No

Q: Did something slow his descent as he traveled down the side of the monument?

A: Yes

Room Despair

A man paid thousands of dollars to build an addition onto his primary residence. Yet, after the construction was completed, he never went into that part of the house again. Why?

Answer, page 227

Clues:

Q: Was he avoiding going into the addition for some reason?

A: No

Q: Did he have a specific reason for not entering the addition?

A: Yes

Q: Was there something unusual about his house?

A: No

The Pilot's Puzzle

A pilot was in an emergency situation, and needed to land his aircraft in unfamiliar territory. He immediately spotted two possible landing sites, the first of which was a flat and open field. The second site was inhabited by grazing livestock and had a rough terrain. Why, then, did he choose the latter?

Answer, page 225

Clues:

Q: If the pilot had landed on the other field, could it have been life-threatening?

A: Yes

Q: Was the presence of the livestock in the field a deciding factor?

A: Yes

Q: Was the man a military pilot?

A: Yes

Q: Was the man flying during wartime?
A: Yes

An Explosive Situation

While at work one day, a man hears a loud explosion and is thrown hundreds of feet through the air. This is witnessed by many people, but no one attempts to give him aid. Why didn't they help the man? *Answer, page 218*

Clues:

Q: Did the man die in the explosion?
A: No

Q: Were the people who saw what had happened start-led by it?
A: No

Q: Was the man prepared for this explosion?
A: Yes

Q: Had this ever happened to the man before?
A: Yes

Leave It or Not

Elizabeth lives in a neighborhood known for its well-tended and manicured lawns. Yet, for some reason, while Elizabeth is busily raking up leaves from her trees, all of her neighbors are content to simply ignore theirs. Can you explain this situation?
Answer, page 221

Clues:

Q: Is Elizabeth at all concerned about the inaction of her neighbors with regard to their leaves?

A: No

Q: Is the time of year important?

A: Yes

Q: Could Elizabeth have prevented the need to rake up the leaves?

A: Yes

Brainbender #25

What word, expression, or name is depicted below?
Answer, page 220

Shore Sighted

A group of friends sets out for a leisurely day of boating and becomes stranded when the motor dies. The boat has no other means of reaching shore, and isn't equipped with a radio, but the friends do find some flares. Still, although they are within sight of hundreds of people on shore, they are not rescued for several hours. Why does rescue take so long?

Answer, page 228

Clues:

Q: Did the stranded people fire any of the flares to indicate that they needed help?

A: Yes

Q: Were the people on shore able to see the flares?

A: Yes

Q: Did the people on shore think that the flares were being used for some other reason?

A: Yes

The Perfect Crime

Rocky bludgeons an acquaintance to death. He makes no attempt to hide the evidence, and the next day he returns to the scene of the crime along with some mutual friends of the victim. As they arrive at the victim's home, Rocky sees that the police have already discovered the body. Although it could have placed Rocky at great risk of criminal prosecution, he freely admits to having been alone with the victim on the previous day. Why?

Answer, page 225

Clues:

Q: Did Rocky take any steps to hide his crime?

A: No

Q: Is there a way Rocky could have planned this perfect crime?

A: No

Q: Did Rocky actually want to avoid being implicated in the crime?

A: Yes

Brainbender #26

What word, expression, or name is depicted below?

Answer, page 221

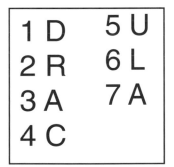

```
1 D      5 U
2 R      6 L
3 A      7 A
4 C
```

Express Checkout

Barry notices a boy and his father in a grocery store, neither of whom he has ever seen before. Although he doesn't speak to anyone and there is nothing unusual going on at the time, he calls the police moments later. What compels him to make this call?
Answer, page 218

Clues:

Q: Is it likely this string of events would have taken place in a department store?

A: No

Q: Could this have taken place thirty years ago?

A: No

Q: Does what merchandise Barry was purchasing matter?

A: Yes

Bill's Birthday Surprise

Marion's husband, Bill, was a slob who avoided bathing at all cost. On his wife's birthday, Bill decided to surprise her by taking a bath without having to be asked. Instead of being pleased, Marion was upset. Why? *Answer, page 216*

Clues:

Q: Would Marion have asked Bill to bathe that day?

A: No

Q: Would Marion have been upset if Bill had taken a bath the day before?

A: No

Q: Did Bill fill the tub himself?

A: No

Q: Did anything else unusual happen that day?

A: Yes

GEOMETRICAL
GYRATIONS

Cutting Cloth

Mary has three pieces of cloth, each of which is in the form of a square. The smallest measures 2×2, the next bigger is 3×3, and the biggest is 6×6. Mary wants to cut the three pieces in such a way that she can sew them together again to make a square that measures 7×7.

What is the smallest number of pieces into which Mary will need to cut the original three pieces of cloth?

Answer, page 233

The Military Band

An enormous military band was marching and playing at an official ceremony. At the beginning, the musicians formed a perfect square; that is, there were the same number of ranks and columns. Suddenly they changed formation and became a rectangle in which the number of columns of musicians was greater by 5 than it had been in the previous formation.

How many musicians were there in the band?

Answer, page 234

A Question of Space

Four T-shaped pieces of wood are lying inside a square box as shown in the diagram. The four pieces need to be transferred into another box that is slightly smaller, the dimensions of which are indicated by the dotted line.

If none of the pieces may overlap another, how must they be arranged to fit into the smaller box?

Answer, page 236

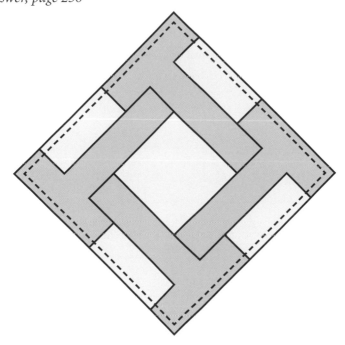

Triangle Salad

Look carefully at the diagram below.

How many different triangles are hidden in it? Hint: There are more than 50. *Answer, page 238*

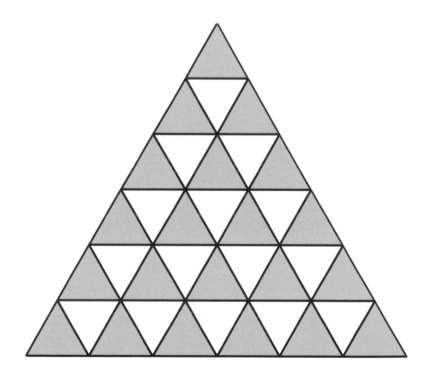

Change of Flag

The diagram below shows the flags of two neighboring countries on Eularia, the largest continent of Iapetus, one of the moons of Saturn. The flags are the same size (9 × 12) and are made up of the same three colors, each of which takes up one third of the area of the flag. On one of the flags the stripes are vertical, while on the other they are horizontal.

How can the flag on the left be cut into four pieces that may then be sewn back together again to make the flag on the right?

Answer, page 235

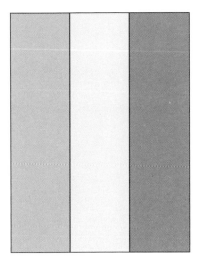 

Two Circles and a Rectangle

How can you draw two circles and a rectangle so that the three shapes intersect in pairs 18 times?

In the diagram below, the triangles and the rectangle intersect each other just 6 times. *Answer, page 239*

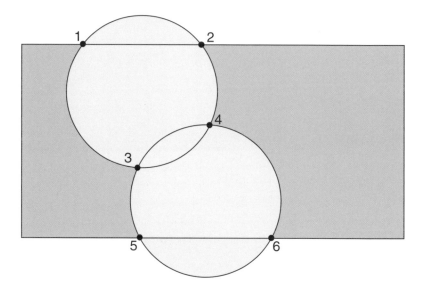

The Jealous Boyfriends

What you see below is the street plan of a little town. The squares marked A, B, C, D, and E indicate the homes of five students who do not get along particularly well with one another. The circles marked with the same letters show where their respective girl-friends live.

What routes should the five students take to visit their girl-friends so that their paths never cross?

Answer, page 236

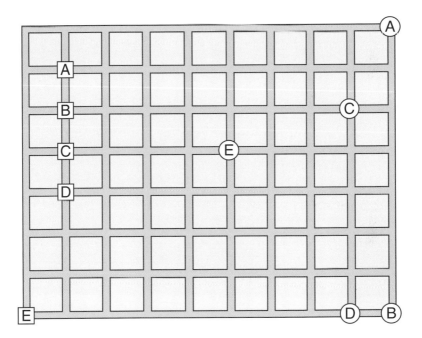

Three Partitions

Divide each of these three regions into three parts that are identical in size and shape. *Answer, page 235*

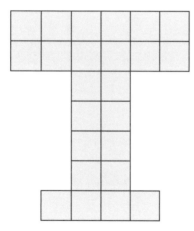

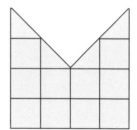

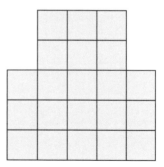

A Spiral of Matches

The spiral in the diagram is made up of 35 matches. The spiral is growing in a clockwise direction. However, by changing the positions of just four of the matches, a spiral can be obtained that grows in the opposite direction.

Which four matches must be changed for the spiral to change direction? *Answer, page 237*

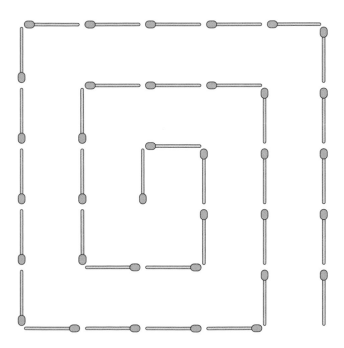

Two Sheets of Paper

Two identical rectangular sheets of paper are lying one on top of the other exactly as shown in the diagram.

Which of the two parts of the sheet of paper underneath is bigger, the part that is uncovered, or the part that is covered?

Answer, page 238

Arthur's Will

Old Arthur owned a perfectly square piece of land in each of whose corners was an inexhaustible well (a, b, c, d). Shortly before he died, Arthur had four identical houses built in a row, as shown in the drawing (A, B, C, D). It was his wish that each of his sons be left one of the houses, and a quarter of the land, with one of the wells on it. In his will, Arthur stipulated that the four pieces of land should have not only the same area but also exactly the same shape.

How must Arthur's land be divided up in order for his wishes to be carried out? *Answer, page 234*

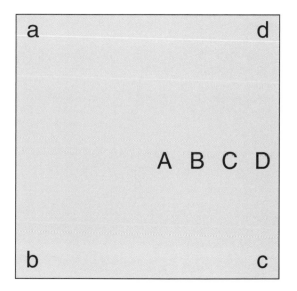

Thirteen Candles

Claude doesn't want anyone to know how old he is unless they do some work. So he designed a birthday cake that uses 13 candles and represents his age.

If you count all of the triangles of all sizes formed by the lines connecting the candles, you will discover Claude's age. Can you figure it out before the candles are blown out?

Answer, page 240

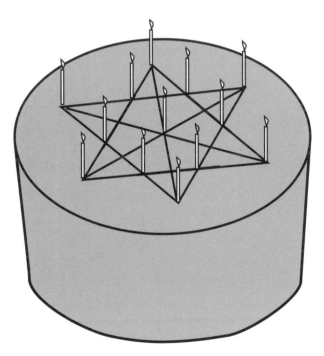

Match Boxes

Which pieces of cardboard below will form boxes if they are folded along the lines? *Answer, page 240*

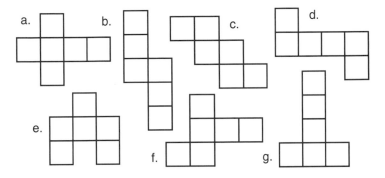

Stick Houses

In case A, can you move one stick and add another to create two matching houses? Case B shows a farmer's pigpen. Can you move two fences and add two more to create two pigpens of the same shape and size? *Answer, page 240*

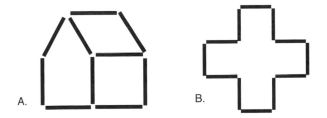

Fit to Be Tiled

Mrs. McGillicutty wants to put tile tops on two large tables. She wants to use tiles of either shape A or shape B. Each square in the tiles is one foot by one foot. The first table is eight by six feet and the second is eight by eight feet. Can you cover both tables according to her wishes without cutting any tiles?

Answer, page 240

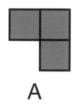

A

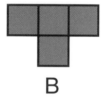

B

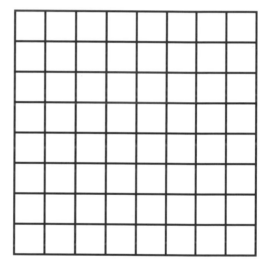

Shot Through the Heart

This (okay, somewhat misshapen) Valentine heart consists of one large semicircle beneath two smaller semicircles. The arrow passes right through the point at which the two smaller semicircles meet.

Which part of the heart's perimeter is the longer: that lying above the line of the arrow, or that lying below?

Answer, page 242

Quilting Bee

If six equilateral triangles each of unit area are joined edge-to-edge, twelve different shapes each of six units in area can be constructed as shown below:

Show that it is impossible to form any six of these shapes into a six-by-six-by-six equilateral triangle of 36 units in area.

Answer, page 245

Flat Tire

A horizontal line from the top of the inside edge of a bicycle tire to the two outside edges of the tire measures 24 centimeters as shown in the side view below:

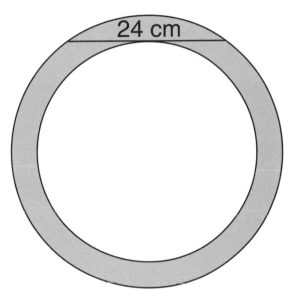

What is the area of the bicycle tire visible from this view?

Answer, page 241

Back to Basics

Two right triangles share the same hypotenuse AB. The shorter sides of the first triangle are 13 and 18 units; the shorter sides of the second are 7 and 20 units.

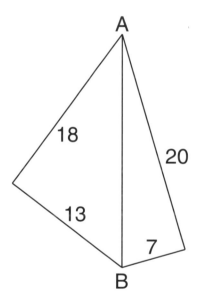

Clearly we are not measuring in base ten. What base is being used, and how long is the hypotenuse?

Answer, page 246

Twinkle, Twinkle

A Christmas decoration comprises a symmetrical four-pointed star supported by three threads. The decoration hangs in the center of a small circular window:

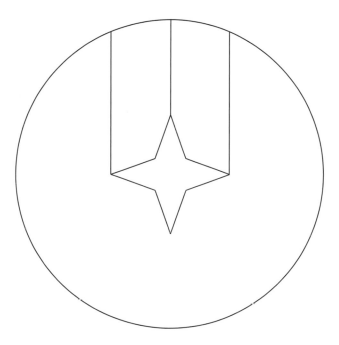

The central thread is 4 centimeters long, and the outer two are each 6 centimeters long. What is the width of the star?

Answer, page 244

Unhinged

Two equal squares, ABCD and DEFG, have the vertex D in common. The angle between the two squares is 60°:

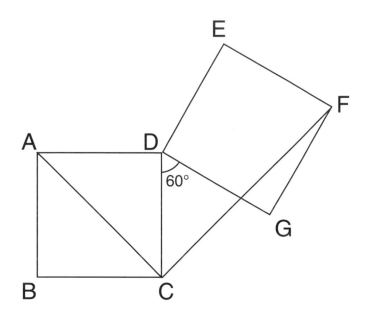

What is the angle ACF? *Answer, page 243*

Go Fish

Eric the Halibut is swimming to the right. Move three sticks (and his eye, smile, and bubbles) so that he is swimming to the left.
Answer, page 245

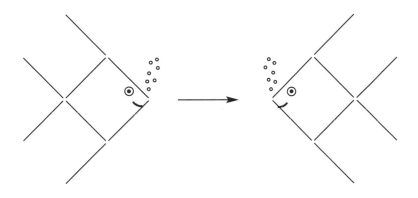

WORDS, WORDS, WORDS

Vowel Exchange

Find back-to-back words with the same number of letters that are spelled alike except for one vowel. Except for the vowel sound, the words are pronounced alike, unlike CODE and CEDE—*code* has a hard C (like "K") and *cede* a soft C (like "S"). We avoid multiple-vowel combinations, like GRIN GREEN. In parentheses is the number of letters of the desired words.

After a vampire BAT BIT me, I needed rabies shots. (3)
The restaurant bandits liked to ROB RIB joints. (3)
The runner LOST LAST year's race. (4)

1. The poker player wanted to _____ _____ he was out of money. (3)

2. After seeing that it wasn't successful, the charity's board of directors decided to _____ _____ as a fund-raising tool. (5)

3. How often do the passengers on a cruise _____ _____ for bargains at local stores when they're at a port? (4)

4. The orchestra had a _____ _____ section. (6)

5. Ship hands raising a _____ _____ know exactly what they're doing. (4)

6. Do people in _____ _____ longer? (4)

7. The stock analyst expected to see manufacturers of the latest computer _____ _____ prices within six months. (4)

8. The _____ _____ skipped out of town before the medical board could find out he wasn't a real doctor. (5)

9. It's hard to watch sailors at a _____ _____ with their loved ones. (4)

10. Is there a handyman I can _____ _____ in the neighborhood? (4)

11. They watched their _____ _____ a hole in the backyard. (3)

12. Prospectors looking for gold _____ _____ scattered throughout this area. (3)

13. People who like to _____ _____ for all kinds of excuses to justify their constant complaining. (5)

14. At the local police _____ _____ of off-duty officers is a major item in their personnel files. (10)

15. Coffee drinkers don't expect a _____ _____. (5)

16. After _____ _____ at the directors' meeting, Mr. Lee received a standing ovation. (5)

17. Did Mrs. O'Leary's cow really make the _____ _____ and start the Chicago fire? (4)

18. *Elite* is among the words that begin _____ _____ with the same vowel. (3)

19. Would a _____ _____ out for small aircraft while flying? (5)

20. The _____ _____ produce water only as clean as the river that feeds it. (4)

Answers, page 247

Rhyme Time

We can create sentences with rhyming words: "Don't FALL over the BALL in the HALL, PAUL." If you're given only the first one or more letters of the word or none at all, finding words that rhyme can be challenging. Consider this sentence:

"Garment manufacturers were GL____ to _____ to their coffers during the F____ to be CL____ in PL____."

The rhyming words *glad, add, fad, clad,* and *plaid* work to make a sensible sentence: "Garment manufacturers were GLAD to ADD to their coffers during the FAD to be CLAD in PLAID." Find the rhyming words that fit in the blanks.

1. Safety is a F____ when asking an _____ to fall from a TR____.

2. His last S____ with his shrink covered modes of EXPR____ of AGGR____.

3. The farmer R____ his crops would be F___ the S____ time around.

4. Did Mr. Wright build a D____ H____ in R____ on sandy L_____?

5. It was her BEL____ that the period of GR____ following a tragedy should be BR____.

6. S____ saw a F____ on the L____ just before D____.

7. If OTH____ were more M____ he'd have been a happier F____.

8. WH____ KN____ Y____ FL____?

9. The G____ was eaten by a M____ on the L____.

10. They advised PER____ to G____ SL____.

11. The Lone Ranger told T____ he needed to get to TOR____ PR____.

12. The last time I played P____ a cigar SM____ kept getting the J_____.

13. She was a firm BEL____ that having a Labrador RETR____ kept her from getting cabin F____.

14. What are the chances of getting SUKIY____ and R____ road ice cream at a H____ game?

15. The MAJ____ of executives with SENI____ are careful not to misuse their AUTH____.

16. The best chance for an ACQU____ is to WH____ away at the prosecution's case a L____ at a time.

17. The lecturer's T____ was how he became MY____ after crossing the TR____ of Capricorn.

18. The golfer started to _____ unprintable words when his P____ began to SP____.

19. The F____ C____ S____ _____ B____ Masterson's table.

20. The police officer caught the fleeing suspect in H____ terrain and knocked him S____ with a B____ club.

Answers, page 248

Broadway Shows

Most Broadway show titles are concise. The Broadway hit show *Rent* sounds better than the would-be description "Monthly Payment Written into a Contract between Lessee and Lessor." Fortunately, such language is suppressed by the playwright or producer's good sense. But what if it were not? Find the original titles for these shows.

1. *The Male of Maximum Degree of Contentment*

2. *Osculate with Me, Katherine*

3. *Automobile Lubrication Chemical*

4. *A Refrain with the Shortest Distance Between Two Points*

5. *Mr. Presley's Nickname and Myself*

6. *Positive Tidings*

7. *Female of Ten Percent of a Decade*

8. *Setting of Nocturnal Variety Entertainment and Imbibing*

9. *Condemn Northerners*

10. *Nocturnal Apparel Diversion*

Answers, page 249

Broadway Songs

Most Broadway song titles are concise. Figure out the original title from the pretentious version of the title below.

1. "Ascend the Complete Set of Precipices"

2. "Express Celestial Gratitude for the Existence of Young Females"

3. "In the Event That a Male First-Person Singular Had a Substantial Net Worth"

4. "The Involuntary Nocturnal Vision That Has a Zero Probability of Occurrence"

5. "Second-Person Singular Will, Under No Circumstance, Perambulate While Unaccompanied"

6. "First-Person Singular Had the Option to Engage in Waltzes, Fox Trots, etc. Throughout the Complete Nocturnal Period"

7. "Randomness, Manifest Yourself as a Female"

8. "A Location Exists for the Specific Benefit of First-Person Plural"

9. "*Homo Sapiens* Will Verbalize Our Mutual Displays of Affection"

10. "Digital Storage Capacity"

Answers, page 249

Buried Song Titles

A nonsense phrase may bury other words. UNSURFACED TENACITY, for example, hides the song title "SURF CITY" buried in the words "unSURFaced tenaCITY." Find the song titles in these nonsense phrases.

1. ENEMY HIDEAWAY

2. COLD UNMANAGEABLE DRIVERS

3. CONDOMINIUM COMPREHENSION COMMISSION

4. FORECLOSED PHOTOGENIC BAYOU

5. VALLEY VACATION

6. AIRBORNE ATOMS ENCUMBER WILDERNESS

7. STEAL COMFORTABLE FLATWORMS

8. CLOVES SUPPLEMENT WISDOM

9. WEATHER'S MOROSE

10. POISONOUS CURARE

Answers, page 250

Call Letters

North American radio and TV stations have three or four call letters. In general, U.S. stations east of the Mississippi River begin with *W,* those west of the Mississippi begin with *K,* those based in Canada begin with *C,* and those based in Mexico begin with *X.*

Using four call letters for imaginary stations, we can have fun matching the four-letter word that the call letters spell out with the station's format or motto. WHIM could be a TV station for impulsive watchers, CLOY a radio station that favors overly sweet and sticky music, and KITE a station for high fliers.

Create appropriate call letters for these would-be stations.

1. The station for Boy Scouts and Girl Scouts

2. The secretly super station

3. The station for hopeful listeners

4. The very end

5. The station that sees right through you

6. The indifferent station

7. The station for royalty

8. The station for chowderheads

9. The studying students' station

10. The Rosebud station

Answers, page 251

Hangwords

In each word puzzle below, some letters have been given. Fill in the letter blanks to make a word. Here are some examples.

```
C __ T T H __ __ __ T          CUTTHROAT
W __ __ __ Z                    WALTZ
__ __ C H N __ Q __ __          TECHNIQUE
```

1. G__ __ B __ G __

2. O __ __ O X __ O __ __

3. __ U __ __ K __ __ Y

4. __ Y R R __

5. F __ A __ H __ __ __ H __

6. __ X Q __ __ S __ __ __

7. G __ __ R K __ __

8. C __ N C __ C __ __ __ N

9. __ B __ Q __ __ __ __ __ __

10. __ __ V __ __ V __ M __ __ __

Answers, page 251

Common Interiors

Sometimes, two words have a common interior. For example, the interior letters of EARTH and PARTY are ART (eARTh, pARTy); inside EFFORT and AFFORD are the letters FFOR.

Find the common interiors of these word pairs.

1. C __ __ __ __ __S & O __ __ __ __ __T

2. C __ __ __ __N & G __ __ __ __L

3. O __ __ __ T & A __ __ __ D

4. J __ __ __ __ Y & R __ __ __ __ D

5. C __ __ __ B & B __ __ __ P

6. E __ __ H & B __ __ K

7. A __ __ __ N & F __ __ __ R

8. C __ __ __ E & M __ __ __ R

9. G __ __ __ T & P __ __ __ O

10. P __ __ __ E & C __ __ __ M

Answers, page 252

Repeaters

A few words in the English language begin with a letter or a combination of letters that's immediately repeated. Examples include AARDVARK, RERECORD, and MURMURING. Try to find "repeaters" that logically complete these sentences.

1. The green salad contained lettuce, celery, and _____.

2. The wind can make _____ sounds when it blows through canyons.

3. New software was used to produce those _____ graphics.

4. Will your trip to Italy include a _____ visit?

5. She had a nonspeaking part in *Conan the* _____.

6. The room contained a futon and a _____ mat.

7. They drank pure red-orange _____ juice every day in Hawaii.

8. Most Chinese restaurants serve black _____ tea.

9. The _____ were ringing their bells.

10. The _____ of the end of the world has embarrassed many cult leaders.

11. Some people prefer a cup of hot _____ to coffee.

12. Some adults love to _____ the books they enjoyed during childhood.

13. The oil that's _____ onto the driveway will cause a stain.

14. The florist sold many roses and _____ last year.

15. Children often _____ their parents.

16. Sometimes, the best-lit room in the aquarium contains the _____.

17. It can be fascinating watching an insect emerge from its _____.

18. The vacation package includes a _____ ride near Macchu Picchu.

19. The con man promised that the investment would return _____ of money.

20. A piña colada typically contains blended rum, pineapple, and _____.

Answers, page 252

Crazy Z

These sentences all contain words with one or more Z's in them. Find words or names with the crazy Z's that make sense in the sentence. Here's an example: The barber said, "I'll cut that hair down to __ __ Z __" and gave me a __ __ ZZ cut. The missing *Z* words are *SIZE* and *BUZZ*.

1. Mom took a pepperoni __ __ Z Z __ out of the __ __ __ __ Z __ __.

2. Despite the __ __ __ __ Z, the quarterback got the ball to his receiver in the end Z __ __ __.

3. If you back up your data on a Z __ __ drive, there's a Z __ __ __ chance that any of it will be lost.

4. I was too __ __ Z __ to go to the Z __ __ today.

5. The video-game player tried to Z __ __ a __ __ Z __ __ bad guys with his laser beam.

6. I learned about former Presidents like John
   __ __ __ Z __ __ __ __ __ __   Kennedy and
   Z __ __ __ __ __ __ Taylor.

7. Witch __ __ Z __ __ never __ __ Z __ __ off while she was
   flying on her broom.

8. Cleaning the __ __ Z __ after an oil spill can be a safety
   __ __ Z __ __ __.

9. __ __ __ Z __ __ is in South America and
   __ __ Z __ __ __ __ __ __ __ is in Africa.

10. It was too __ __ Z __ outside to __ __ Z __ at the
    mountains.

Answers, page 253

Food Words

The sentence "Is _____ the list of the top ten Italian tourist cities?" can be completed with a food word, VENISON (Venice on). The sentence "They would not _____ _____ inside without our press credentials" can be completed with LETTUCE (let us). You may remember the old riddle about not starving in the desert because of all the SANDWICH is there. Find a food word to complete these sentences.

1. If we _____ this year, let's have a formal wedding next year.

2. Her only living relatives are a sister in Boston and _____ in Newark.

3. Mr. Mineo's agent said, "Let _____ some of his own dialogue."

4. The division that suffered the biggest budget _____ half their staff go.

5. If the loggers keep up the current _____ clearance in this section will be completed in three weeks.

6. Did an obsessed fan ever try to _____ Nova singer Astrud Gilberto?

7. If everybody would _____ or a dime more into the economy every day, there would be more employment.

8. When the ratings on her show _____ Tyler Moore formed a production company.

9. The line drive down the third base line landed _____.

10. They loved to watch Fred and _____ dance.

11. The witness saw the _____ up to the victim and stab him.

12. The dog tried to _____ his bone.

13. At the end of his contract _____ Estrada decided not to do any more episodes of *CHIPS.*

14. Her grandparents always used to give up meat from _____ Easter Sunday.

15. Do all Wal-Mart executives have a portrait of _____ the wall in their offices?

16. Mr. and Mrs. Sampras once said, "_____ sure bet to become a top tennis player."

17. Even though Tom Hanks often acts like a _____ Ryan enjoys co-starring with him.

18. The choice was to stay in the air-conditioned room or to _____ the hot sun outside.

19. If Rocky Balboa saw Alice B. Toklas's significant other, he'd probably yell, "_____!"

20. She was too young to remember _____ Jeff.

Answers, page 254

Automotive Words

The sentence "If the hatchet is too small, the _____ get the job done" can be completed with a car-related word or name—axle (ax'll). "The Scrabble® player got a good score by placing an _____ a triple letter square" can be completed with *Exxon* (X on). Try to find a car-related word or name for these sentences.

1. The home video of the children running the hundred-yard _____ them to tears.

2. Why _____ be the only freeze-dried orange juice product that this store sells?

3. Most trombones have slides, but some have _____.

4. They drove from Cannes to _____ their French Riviera honeymoon.

5. It takes a lot of selling off of stocks to _____ market into a bear market.

6. Did a realtor negotiate the sale of the _____ Chemical Company bought for its largest factory?

7. The merchant hoped that most of the sailors in the _____ be regular customers when they came back to their homeport.

8. Movie fans watched Richard _____ from being a heartthrob in *Pretty Woman* to being a villain in *Nowhere to Hide*.

9. Travel guides usually _____ rates for the hotels they describe.

10. Did _____ Larry and Curly a lot of stories?

11. At news conferences, politicians tend to _____ difficult questions.

12. It's difficult for accountants to take long _____ during tax season.

13. At the directors' convention, some people heard Federico Fellini and Carlo _____ all night long about their past accomplishments.

14. The poker player stayed in the pot with only an ace _____ too long.

15. Will the rancher to whom you sold the diseased _____ your neck when he finds out the truth?

16. The more conservative horse racing gambler might say, "When you're at the _____ the long shots and just bet on the favorites."

17. Frank Sinatra sang, "When I was seventeen, it was a very _____."

18. Can a salesperson who is _____ as well as one who is wordy?

19. Did her Siamese _____ hole in her sweater when he scratched it?

20. I don't want to hear another _____ story.

Answers, page 255

Computer Talk

The sentence "The boxing champion faced many challengers, but he _____ all down" can be completed with a word in computer jargon—*modem* (mowed 'em). The sentence "Don't ever _____

I'll wash out your mouth with soap and water" can be completed with *cursor* (curse or). Try to find a word in computer jargon to complete these sentences.

1. Were both father and _____ when they fell asleep at the play last night?

2. After the first inning, the Yankees were ahead one _____.

3. Was Jack _____ a perfect 20–20 when he starred in *Dragnet?*

4. Did the new fishing _____ as well as the old one?

5. A male ovine is more commonly called a _____.

6. How often did Nikita speak to _____ the red phone?

7. The soldiers who were supposed to protect the _____ away instead.

8. Her favorite disaster movie was *Krakatoa East of* _____.

9. The Ambassador will be _____ Aviv all of next week.

10. The Irish musician said, "Happiness is a _____ to eat and three or four groupies."

11. Charles didn't like to be called _____.

12. Rather than risk his next season being a _____ Wee Reese retired from baseball.

13. It's a long _____ from New York to Miami.

14. Does the wooden _____ twice as much as the aluminum one?

15. The city council decided to take _____ school funding issues at the next session.

16. There was a new challenge _____ Dillon during every episode of *Gunsmoke.*

17. He tried reading the latest bestseller, but he just couldn't get _____.

18. There were no cold cuts in the refrigerator, so he opened a can of _____.

19. The shirts are available in S, M, L, and _____.

20. _____ a sorrowful thing to realize how few people appreciate Shakespearean English.

Answers, page 256

World Capitals

The sentence "Some of Mr. Preminger's friends wanted to throw _____ surprise party" can be completed with the name of a world capital—*Ottawa* (Otto a). The sentence "She fancied herself a blend of Gypsy Rose _____ Barker and Mata Hari" can be completed with *Lima* (Lee, Ma). Find a world capital to complete these sentences.

1. Many years ago, we saw George Burns joking with Milton _____ the Friar's Club.

2. That would make _____ years old and Mama seventy-six years old.

3. The driver was the _____ survivor of the crash.

4. _____ be the only catcher who had a cartoon bear named after him?

5. _____ Moffo and Kathleen Battle made the critic's list of the ten all-time best sopranos?

6. Did the customer with the silk paisley _____ for it before he left the store?

7. Smart merchants _____ improvement stores with many brands of tools.

8. After her marriages to Richard Burton, how many times has _____ divorced?

9. There was a Santa Claus suit in the shopping _____ brought home a few days before Christmas.

10. Is _____ the top-ten list of mantras?

11. A commercial machine should be capable of _____ after ton of dirty clothing.

12. The medium claimed to be able to communicate with the ghost of Marilyn _____ her seances.

13. Is _____ the widest shoe that's sold here?

14. Some spouses are faithful, but others _____.

15. If a police officer catches you making _____ is almost certain to follow.

16. Did one of Ms. Tucker's fans actually give _____ diamond ring?

17. What's a fair price for 100 one-third cut legal-size _____ file folders?

18. Sometimes the captain has to _____ ship in choppy waters.

19. The veteran of the Korean _____ many of his buddies get killed.

20. The dentist thought that if the plaque could be kept at _____ canal work could be avoided.

Answers, page 257

Name Games

Some people's first names can be used as words that name an animal or object or describe an action, object, event, or animal. These sentences contain both. Tom couldn't tell if he were eating a tom or a hen turkey. Flo was asked to "go with the flow."

These sentences begin with a name that's also used as a word later in the same sentence. The second word may be spelled the same way or appear as a *homonym* (a word that sounds the same but is spelled differently). Fill in the blanks with names and words that create good, sensible sentences.

1. _____ liked to use a hand-held _____ when he was making a speech.

2. _____ had just two days to learn a new Christmas _____.

3. _____ stayed home from school because her temperature _____ above 99° F.

4. _____ decided not to _____ a mask for Halloween.

5. _____ liked the lasagna, but his sister thought it was a _____ too spicy.

6. _____ took a trip to Yellowstone Park and the Medicine _____ mountains.

7. _____ learned that some people use "et _____" instead of "et cetera."

8. _____ was trying to memorize the _____ of Rights.

9. _____ and his parents went to an _____ museum.

10. _____ has an uncle who's a lawyer who likes to _____ people.

Answers, page 258

Reversible Words

Some words, when spelled backwards, give us a different word. These aren't palindromes (like POP or SEES), and since they don't have a fancy name, we'll call them "reversible words." Examples are REWARD or DRAWER and ON or NO. The word REWARD when reversed spells DRAWER. The "reverse" of ON is NO. These sentences have reversible words:

The sheriff found an old REWARD poster in a dresser DRAWER.

When the judge is seated ON the bench, there must be NO talking.

Fill the blanks in these sentences with reversible words (first spelled one way then in reverse) so that they make good sense.

1. _____ is as selfless as I _____.

2. There is a _____ of leftover stew on the _____ shelf of the refrigerator.

3. ____ is well-known that "_____" is the note after "la."

4. The beaver got _____ at animals that disturbed his _____.

5. I was so hungry that I ate my _____ sandwich on the _____.

6. Kittens are great _____ as long as you don't _____ on them.

7. I went to ____; then I dreamed about clowns tripping on banana _____.

8. The rock _____ kept mice and _____ as pets.

9. Sometimes a _____ of calamine lotion can soothe a _____ itch.

10. The _____ _____ not in the tool shed, where it belonged.

11. The quick brown fox said, " _____ no!" as the riders yelled, "Tally _____!"

12. It's _____ to stay off ski lifts and _____ while they're being repaired.

13. The best _____ of the story was watching the hero _____ the spy.

14. There was some _____ stuck on Mom's coffee _____.

15. Yes, you _____ have another _____ after you finish your turkey.

16. The bully had no friends because he always tried to _____ his _____.

17. My aunts sometimes make a big _____ over who _____ a better sweater.

18. My Chihuahua is a great _____ so I let him sit on my _____.

19. We _____ about to study the _____ of the dinosaur.

20. After _____ tries, I finally served the ball over the _____.

21. Dad wanted to _____ my paper about how the _____ is affected by the moon.

22. When my uncle is in a bad _____, he talks about gloom and
    _____.

23. I'd rather _____ for gold than take a _____.

24. There's a rumor that _____ people _____ in the old house.

25. The mail carrier was _____ by his boss for failure to _____
    the mail on time.

26. A _____ that's heavier than air will _____ down to the bottom of a mineshaft.

27. Even a heavy television set does _____ weigh a _____.

28. He _____ yesterday but he's losing right _____.

29. Mom secured the bicycle _____ to the luggage rack with a
    thick _____.

30. If you think that silly mask will _____ anybody, you're _____.

31. I didn't _____ washing the _____ until they were
    completely clean.

32. I _____ up my skates and took a speck of mud off the gold
    _____.

33. I'd never _____ a pet with _____ for one with fins.

34. I got a _____ that eating the inside of a peach _____ is bad
    for you.

35. My little brother plays with _____ toys, _____ I outgrew them.

36. Uranium can _____ a lot of radiation over a long period of _____.

37. If I _____ you on the shoulder, please pass me a _____ of butter.

38. I'm sure it's hard to train a _____ to push the _____ key.

39. You're more likely to find swimming _____ on an ocean liner than on a _____.

40. Sports-car owners like to _____ their _____ exhausts.

Answers, page 258

Cities & States

Each of the fifty states in the U.S. is presented here with two questions. Fill in the blank with the name of a city in the state mentioned.

Do you know how many _____ Evans got after falling off her horse in New York?
   Scarsdale (scars Dale)

Were many SAT scores above the _____ Oklahoma?
   Norman (norm in)

Find a one-word city or town in the state that completes the two questions for each of the fifty states.

1. How many _____ Ward stores were in Alabama?

2. Did the insurance salesman try to _____ and Pa a new policy in Alabama?

3. Is it legal to use a _____ de plume in Alaska?

4. Did a member of Steely _____ any treasure in Connecticut?

5. Was "The White Cliffs of _____" recorded in Delaware?

6. Was it appropriate to let the lawyers for Paula _____ so deep into Bill Clinton's past in Arkansas?

7. Is it true that _____ allowed to enter a guy's restroom in Arizona?

8. Was the _____ paid for a local paper a fair price in Arizona?

9. Can an automobile collector buy a _____ Torme once owned in California?

10. Was 3Com Stadium Dusty _____ of choice in California?

11. Can a brave person act even _____ in Colorado?

12. Do most restaurants give you a twist of _____ your Perrier in Colorado?

13. At what time of year is the ice so thin you can neither skate _____ safely in Connecticut?

14. Do people who want to get married in _____ they need to book a catering hall well in advance in Alaska?

15. Do local residents _____ to build a Presidential library in Arkansas?

16. Do tennis players get upset when they _____ in Delaware?

17. If a songwriter _____ jingle for Pepsi, will he or she become rich and famous in Florida?

18. Would an updated version of the parting of the Red _____ more tourists into Universal Studios in Florida?

19. Was she really _____ a lot of money or just talkin' a lot of nonsense in Georgia?

20. Is _____ hot month in Georgia?

21. _____ hotel be allowed to overbook rooms in Hawaii?

22. Does anybody know _____ Dee and Elton John never performed a duet in Hawaii?

23. Do children's shoe stores carry all the widths from a girl's triple A to a _____ in Idaho?

24. Is it true that after the war in _____ returned to Ma and the kids in Idaho?

25. Did _____ back too far in his chair and fall on Curly in Illinois?

26. Did Lerner and Lowe write "The Night They Invented _____" in Illinois?

27. Is parental consent required for sixteen-year-olds to _____ Indiana?

28. Was the _____ *Moore Show* seen by many people in Indiana?

29. How often do goal-setting executives achieve their _____ in Iowa?

30. Is a _____ usually surrounded by loveseats in Iowa?

31. Are shoppers allowed _____ long time in store windows in Kansas?

32. Do voters tend to be _____ in Kansas?

33. Are there any volcanoes in Kentucky, and, if so, where would the volcanic _____ after an eruption?

34. Has _____ Henderson ever starred in *The Sound of Music* in Kentucky?

35. Are _____ cheese croissants heavily spiced in Louisiana?

36. Do history students learn about the _____ Doctrine in Louisiana?

37. Did the firecracker go _____ did it fail to explode in Maine?

38. Has a Beatles fan ever shaken hands with Lennon _____ in Maine?

39. Do you think _____ still put on teachers' desks in Maryland?

40. Do houses face _____ often than east in Maryland?

41. Did William Randolph ever say "I _____" in Massachusetts?

42. Do I have to repeat myself over _____ again in Massachusetts?

43. Would Batman be able to live as Bruce _____ in Michigan?

44. Have there been any fallow _____ in Michigan?

45. Was *The Jack Benny Show* with Don Wilson, Dennis Day, and _____ popular in Minnesota?

46. Did anybody care what kind of _____ Kaelin was in Minnesota?

47. Do you think that hitting a shot off the _____ be a good reason to break a golf club in Mississippi?

48. Can you open a game of draw poker with a pair of _____ Mississippi?

49. Did Janis _____ ever do a concert in Missouri?

50. Do people try to transfer property _____ names to avoid taxes in Missouri?

51. Did Ms. Keller's relatives try to find _____ place to live in Montana?

52. Do doctors use bookkeeping services to handle their _____ in Montana?

53. Are there books about anthropology and the search for the missing _____ Nebraska?

54. Is it true that with proper medical _____ injuries can be successfully treated in Nebraska?

55. Do students learn about Ulysses S. Grant and Robert _____ in Nevada?

56. Did Skitch _____ and the Tonight Show Band ever play in Nevada?

57. Do many people know what kind of _____ Arthur was in everyday life in New Hampshire?

58. Is there any place to land a _____ Jet in New Hampshire?

59. Was Senator Lott simply called _____ New Jersey?

60. Would a latter-day Noah ever try to build a _____ in New Jersey?

61. Would an arrested thug _____ his buddies in New Mexico?

62. Do many people participate in the _____ Poll in New Mexico?

63. Are _____ Goodman's recordings available in music stores in New York?

64. If _____ man off, is he likely to try to get back at you in New York?

65. Which bakery sells the best _____ Russe in North Carolina?

66. Is it true that the Mad _____ the most popular *Alice in Wonderland* character in North Carolina?

67. Do the production people in show _____ down many good shoot sites when they're in North Dakota?

68. Did Green Bay quarterback Brett _____ to school in North Dakota?

69. Is it easy for high school seniors to find a prom _____ Ohio?

70. Did Elmer Gantry ever deliver any of his _____ Ohio?

71. Did anybody besides Ms. Field see what _____ in Oklahoma?

72. Is it customary to _____ person in trouble in Oklahoma?

73. Can ships from a foreign _____ in Oregon?

74. Do government employees often _____ the rules in granting building permits in Oregon?

75. When should I tell _____ will be going to visit her mother in Pennsylvania?

76. Do winds most often blow in from the _____ Pennsylvania?

77. Is a _____ going to be needed to handle the next generation of cargo ships in Rhode Island?

78. Did the _____ Trio ever play in Rhode Island?

79. Would a solid marble _____ typical architectural feature in mansions in South Carolina?

80. Would a _____ more on a prison scale than on a home scale in South Carolina?

81. Can one find a good Bartlett or Bosc _____ in South Dakota?

82. Did the Chad _____ Trio ever perform in South Dakota?

83. How can horse racing be a _____ if there are no monarchs in Tennessee?

84. Do oldies stations still play "The _____ Stomp" in Tennessee?

85. Is it better to use _____ linoleum on kitchen floors in Texas?

86. How did the _____ Powers movies do in Texas?

87. Are there any celebrations of the day of the _____ equinox in Utah?

88. Did _____ Nash ever recite "Candy Is Dandy" in Utah?

89. Can a pilot who's in a _____ safely in Vermont?

90. Is there a safe place to _____ my goods when I'm in Vermont?

91. Do office supply stores usually have _____ machine pricing in Virginia?

92. Is it easy for a tired person to get some _____ Virginia?

93. Do pet groomers usually find it difficult _____ long-haired dog in rainy weather in Washington?

94. Would anybody understand me if I _____ Arabic dialect in Washington?

95. Do many mothers spend time _____ their babies in old-fashioned carriages in West Virginia?

96. Do Boy Scouts spend much time _____ cans and other debris on the trails in West Virginia?

97. How quickly _____ close down an unsafe factory in Wisconsin?

98. Who played Oscar _____ in the revival of *The Odd Couple* in Wisconsin?

99. Would his _____ the two-step with his neighbor's daughter in Wyoming?

100. Can you imagine _____ and Dr. Zhivago all together in Wyoming?

Answers, page 260

IT'S LOGICAL

Losing Track

On this animal track quiz, one student copied his or her answers from the other three students. By looking at their answers below, you should be able to tell who cheated.

Ironically, the cheater got none of the answers correct. If the other students had two correct answers each, what are the correct answers?

The Question:
Match these five tracks to the animals that made them.

The Answers:
ART: 1. deer 2. caribou 3. mt. goat 4. moose 5. bison
BOB: 1. caribou 2. moose 3. deer 4. bison 5. mt. goat
CAT: 1. bison 2. mt. goat 3. deer 4. caribou 5. moose
DEB: 1. deer 2. moose 3. mt. goat 4. caribou 5. bison

Answer, page 269

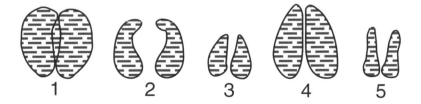

Detective Story

"Detective Slooth? This is Sergeant Chiller from Thunder Bay. We have been tracking a jewelry thief and he's headed south toward you. He is driving a red Honda Civic above the speed limit and he's dressed for the weather, which is 30 degrees. I hope you can help us intercept him before he pawns off the goods."

Detective Slooth sees a red Honda Civic coming into Duluth, but the driver is wearing shorts and a tank top. What should he do?
Answer, page 269

Categorically Speaking

The 25 words below are the answers to a game of Categories. That is, each of them fits one of five categories and begins with one of five letters. Can you reconstruct the categories and arrange the words so that each category contains a word beginning with each letter?
Answer, page 267

MAGENTA CORAL   MANGO
AMETHYST SHELL CHESTNUT
SNOWBALL PURPLE MUSSEL
CANDY CAMELLIA SPRUCE
ANEMONE MAGNOLIA   PAIL
PALM SAND SCARLET CHAIR
MYRTLE AMARYLLIS APPLE
PEARL PRIMROSE AMBER

Get the Scoop

Ken and Terry's, the local ice cream shop, will be giving away free cones some time this year. Because they want to limit the lines a bit, they have given out three clues as to the date of their giveaway. Can you figure out when it will be?

- The giveaway will be in the first week of a month without an A in it.

- It will be on a day of the week that has a U in it.

- The month has no E but the day of the week contains an E.

Answer, page 269

Fit for a Princess

Young Princess Figleaf of Lalaland has four pieces of jewelry that are family heirlooms: a necklace, a ring, a bracelet, and a brooch. Being a fashion-conscious noble, she doesn't like to wear the same thing twice.

How many different combinations of crown jewels can Princess Figleaf wear? She may wear any number of jewels at a time.

Answer, page 269

Ruff and Ready

At the recent running of the Doggie Jog, every person ran with at least one dog. The organizers want to know how many dogs and people participated. Unfortunately, the photographer tripped as he took the group picture, and got a shot of the racers' feet, but nothing else. A reporter in a helicopter scanned the canines and humans from above, but his scanner picked up only the total number of eyes. If the photographer counted 196 feet and paws and the reporter tallied 126 eyes, how many people and how many dogs ran the race? *Answer, page 271*

Alligator Ally

Use logic to figure out which is the alligator and which is the crocodile. One of them is telling the truth and one is lying.
Answer, page 267

Pie-Eyed

Grandma said she'd make her homemade cherry pie if you can figure out this problem: Given three bowls and 12 cherries, can you
arrange the fruit so that there are an odd number of cherries in each
bowl? Oh, and each bowl must contain more than three cherries.
Answer, page 270

Orchestration

In the Pinedale Orchestra, there are 14 violinists and 8 cellists. Of
those orchestra members, 5 belong to the Fencing Club and half
are in the Snake Lovers Association. Of the 14 orchestra members
in the clubs, only 2 belong to both, neither of whom are cellists. If
6 violinists are in neither club and 3 cellists are in the snake
group, how many violinists are fencers? And how many cellists
belong to neither club? *Answer, page 270*

Concentration

There are eight pairs of cards ranked two through nine in this game of Concentration. Given the hints shown below and the two cards that are overturned, can you figure out where all of the pairs are?

1. No pairs appear in the same row or column.
2. No pairs appear in the same long diagonal.
3. The fourth column has only even numbers.
4. The second column has only odd numbers.
5. The first row contains the numbers 2 to 5.
6. The second row contains the numbers 6 to 9.
7. The corners contain the numbers 2 to 5.
8. There is a 3 in the upper left corner and a 4 in the lower right corner.

Answer, page 268

Calendar Girls

Lydia and her friends are trying to find a good time for the next meeting of their investment club. Looking at next month, and the obligations that the five women already have, which weekday evening (or evenings) are possible meeting times?

- Lydia has volleyball games on Tuesdays and Thursdays.
- Sophie volunteers with Meals on Wheels every third day starting on the first.
- Daisy is busy every other Friday starting the 3rd and has tickets to concerts on the 15th and 29th.
- Fiona can't meet on Mondays and has book club on the eighth.

Answer, page 267

S	M	T	W	T	F	S
			1	2	3	4
5	6	7	8	9	10	11
12	13	14	15	16	17	18
19	20	21	22	23	24	25
26	27	28	29	30	31	

The Right Direction

Ray and Wendy were driving to a surprise party. Ray knew what part of town they were going to, but he couldn't find the house. They passed Owl Street and it started raining. By the time they drove by Rabbit Court for the third time, it was getting close to 12:00, when the guest was to arrive. Ray asked to see the scrap of paper that the address was written on.

"Aha," he said, "Now I know what the problem is."

Do you?

Answer, page 270

Order, Please

Ms. Carter, the homeroom teacher, lined up six students in the order shown by A. Not satisfied, she rearranged them in the order shown by B. What is the basis for each sequence?

Answer, page 270

	Arlene	Tyler	Barbara	Eric	Christie	Rob
A.	4	3	5	2	6	1
B.	4	1	3	5	6	2

Guesstimation

Guess the number that correctly completes each statement below.

1. There are __ ridges on a quarter.   a. 8
2. There are __ ridges on a dime.   b. 10
3. You can fold a sheet of newspaper in half __ times.   c. 12
4. There are ___ dimples on a golf ball.   d. 20
5. There are __ letters in the Hawaiian alphabet.   e. 118
6. You have to lick __ stamps to consume one calorie.   f. 119
7. The average polar bear lives __ years.   g. 336

Answer, page 269

Whoa, Baby!

Jen gave birth to her daughter Caroline on the first of January in a year following a leap year. Starting in February, on the first of the month throughout that year, she made note of the day of the week. She noticed that the monthly anniversary of her daughter's birth fell on a Friday three times that year. On what day of the week was Caroline born? And how many months old was Caroline before her monthly "birthday" fell on its original day for the third time (not counting her actual day of birth)? *Answer, page 271*

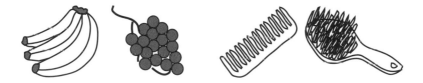

It Takes All Sorts

Kevin likes the opera but not the ballet. He has a boxer but won't get a bulldog. He will travel to Colorado but not Alaska. He collects dimes but not nickels. Does he like bananas or grapes?

Rhonda will go see ballet but not opera. Her favorite number is eight and she doesn't like nine. She likes salmon but not trout. She hates Mondays but likes Wednesdays. Does she use a comb or a brush? *Answer, page 269*

The Chips Are Down

A black cat just knocked all of the chips off of Grandma's bingo card. And she was so close to BINGO, too. There were only five open squares on her card, and yet not one full row or column.

If there were no twos showing and G55 was uncovered, can you put the chips back on the card to show how it looked before the cat stepped on it? *Answer, page 268*

B	I	N	G	O
8	16	43	55	61
13	29	37	56	70
5	24	free	48	72
14	19	35	59	67
1	23	42	50	71

Phone-y Words

Each number in the grid below stands for one of three letters, as shown on the telephone buttons. Four four-letter words read across and four four-letter words read down. Each number stands for a different letter reading across than down. What unique set of common, uncapitalized words will fill the grid? *Answer, page 270*

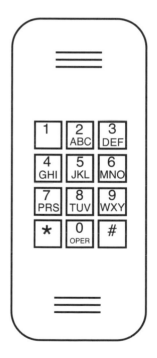

8	4	5	9
3	6	6	3
2	2	6	3
5	4	2	7

Seeds of Doubt

Early this spring, Mrs. Rowe planted a 3 × 4 square-foot garden with six different vegetables. Now, a few sprouts are coming up, but she doesn't remember where the potatoes are.

Using the clues and the map of the garden, can you figure out which squares hold potatoes?

1. Each vegetable uses a 2 × 1 foot plot of adjacent squares.
2. Spinach has sprouted in A1.
3. Cucumbers are coming up in A2.
4. Basil is budding in B2.
5. Every plant in column C is different.
6. Peas are popping up in C3.
7. Onions are on their way in D3.

Answer, page 271

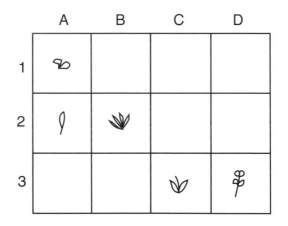

Clock Wise

While staying at a friend's house, you notice that there are three clocks in the bedroom, but they all show different times.

When you ask your friend for the correct time, he yells from the kitchen, "One clock is 20 minutes fast, one is slow, and one is off by 30 minutes, but I forget in which direction."

What time is it? *Answer, page 268*

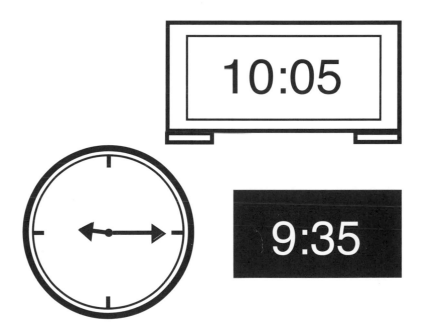

Three Cards

Three playing cards, taken from a normal pack, are placed face-down on a table in a row. To the right of a king there are one or two queens. To the left of a queen there are one or two queens. To the left of a heart there are one or two spades. To the right of a spade there are one or two spades.

Which three cards are we talking about? *Answer, page 271*

True or False

Determine which of the following statements are true and which are false. *Answer, page 272*

1. Exactly one of the statements in this list is false.
2. Exactly two of the statements in this list are false.
3. Exactly three of the statements in this list are false.
4. Exactly four of the statements in this list are false.
5. Exactly five of the statements in this list are false.
6. Exactly six of the statements in this list are false.
7. Exactly seven of the statements in this list are false.
8. Exactly eight of the statements in this list are false.
9. Exactly nine of the statements in this list are false.
10. Exactly ten of the statements in this list are false.

The Cycle Race

In a 14-stage cycle race there were 100 competitors, among them "Crazy" Charles.

In all 14 stages "Crazy" Charles finished in the same position: 93rd. However, at the end of the race, "Crazy" Charles was declared runner-up in the competition: his accumulated time was less than that of all the other competitors except one, the champion.

Bearing in mind the fact that none of the 100 competitors withdrew from the race, how was it possible for "Crazy" Charles to finish second if he never even made it into the top 90 competitors?
Answer, page 274

Three Thorny Matters

- Suppose someone says to you: "I bet you a hundred dollars that if you pay me five hundred dollars, I'll give you back a thousand dollars." Should you make the bet?

- This sentense contains two mistakes. What are the mistakes?

- One glass is half full of wine and another glass is half full of water. A spoonful of wine is taken from the first glass and poured into the glass containing the water. From the resulting mixture a spoonful is taken and dropped into the glass containing the wine. Is the quantity of wine in the glass of water now more or less than the quantity of water in the glass of wine?

Answer, page 275

Three Sisters

"How old are your three daughters?" Fred asked a friend one day.

"The product of their ages is 36," replied his friend.

"You are not giving me enough information," protested Fred.

"The sum of their ages is the age of your oldest son."

"I still need more information."

"All right, then. I can tell you that the oldest daughter, who is at least a year older than the other two, is a very fine pianist."

"Ah! Now I know how old your daughters are."

What are the ages of Fred's friend's daughters?

Answer, page 276

The Incomplete Grid

The grid shown is made up of 104 small squares arranged in a rectangle of 8 by 13 squares. Many of the squares are dark, and the rest are light. However, in the drawing only eight of the squares that should be dark are filled in.

Above each column, a number indicates the number of squares in that column that are dark, while on the left of each row, another number indicates the number of squares in that row that are dark.

Which squares in the grid are dark? *Answer, page 274*

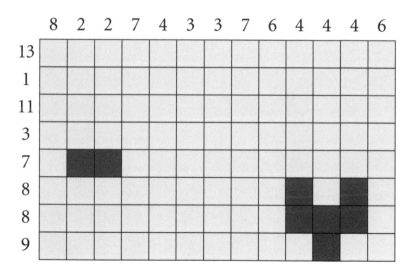

Athletes' Tales

Four athletes, Ann, Bea, Carol, and Dorothy went out one morning and ran a race. At the end of the race, the following statements were made:

Ann: "I didn't come in first or last."

Bea: "I didn't come in last."

Carol: "I was first."

Dorothy: "I was last."

It is known that one, and one only, of the four athletes is lying. Who won the race? *Answer, page 273*

The Ball

Four brothers go to a dance. As they leave, each one of the brothers accidentally takes a hat belonging to another brother and a coat belonging to another, different, brother. Maurice takes the coat belonging to the brother whose hat got taken by Phil, while Phil's coat got taken by the brother who took Maurice's hat. Serge took John's hat.

Whose coats and hats were taken by Maurice and Phil?
Answer, page 276

The Football Fans

Thirty fans hire a bus to attend a football game. On the way to the stadium they realize that exactly half of them are fans of one team, and the other half are fans of the other team. With still some way to go before reaching the stadium, the bus develops mechanical problems and the driver announces to his passengers that the only way to continue the journey is for half of them to get out and walk. There is a huge fight that doesn't stop until the driver speaks to them again and suggests a way of selecting the passengers who are to get off the bus.

"All of you," he said, "get into a big circle. When you are ready, beginning at this spot, I'll count nine people clockwise. The ninth person leaves the circle and continues on foot. Then I'll count another nine starting from where I stopped, and the ninth person leaves the circle and continues on foot. And so on until fifteen people have left the circle."

Suppose that you are one of the fans. How should you arrange all the other fans of your team so that none of them will have to walk?

Answer, page 272

The Portrait of an Unknown Man

One man shows another the portrait of a gentleman and tells him: "I have neither brothers nor sisters, but this man's father is the son of my father."

Who is the man in the painting? *Answer, page 272*

The Drama Festival

Eleven theater groups took part in a festival. Every day some of the groups put on their plays while the others watched. When the festival was over it was possible to affirm that each one of the groups had been able to attend, at least once, the performances of each of the other groups.

What is the minimum number of days that the festival lasted?

Answer, page 273

Two Mistaken Students

A teacher writes a whole number less than 50,000 on the blackboard. One student states that the number is a multiple of 2; a second student states the number is a multiple of 3; and so on until a twelfth student says that it is a multiple of 13. The teacher remarks that all except two of the students were right and, moreover, that the two who were wrong spoke one after the other.

What was the number that the teacher wrote on the blackboard? *Answer, page 275*

The False Coin

You are given 18 silver coins but you find out that one of the coins (you don't know which) is fake and weighs less than any of the others.

How can you be able to detect the false coin using a normal balance scale only three times? *Answer, page 271*

ANSWERS

VISUAL TEASERS

Animal Strength (page 4)

The frogs will win the third tug of war. Two turtles will tie with four frogs.

Attention, Shoppers (page 36)

Lusina bought the atlas, hat, lamp, and iron.

Beady Eyes (page 26)

8,888 was added to abacus A (8,375) to get the sum on abacus B (17,263).

Black and White (page 14)

1. You have two white cards.
2. You have one white card and one black card. (If you had two black cards, A would know what he had on the second round, because if he had two of the same card, one of you would have seen four of one color and known you had two of the other color.)

Blind Alleys (page 7)

They started in Redland.

Block Party (page 6)

She took the "CUBE ROUTE."

Catch a Code (page 22)

HE FELT REMORSE (re"Morse.")

Circular Notions (page 37)

1. ERUCTATION (count 7 squares at a time)
2. OMPHALOSKEPSIS (count 3 squares at a time)

Domino Effect (page 24)

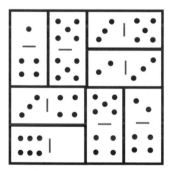

Rotations of this arrangement also work.

Draw by Numbers (page 30)

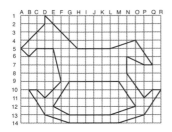

Fishing Lines (page 13)

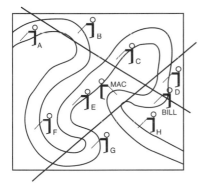

Game Plan (page 16)

A: Player X wins; B: Player X wins (X plays above O first, then no matter where O plays, X can either win on the next turn or take the lowest empty right-hand box and win on the following turn).

Go for a Spin (page 33)

1: jaw, ear, hip, toe, arm, and leg.
2: ape, gnu, pig, elk, fox, and yak.

Gone to Pieces (page 40)

1. alligator; 2. giraffe; 3. gorilla; 4. whale; 5. whale; 6. seal;
7. gorilla; 8. elephant; 9. zebra; 10. rhinoceros.

Irish Eyes (page 18)

Jollos and Plotz (page 19)

Jollos have a circle, triangle, and two lines; plotz have a circle and
four lines. A and C are plotz.

Jumper Cables (page 21)

Stan and Jan are grabbing the same rope.

Key Rings (page 18)

A. yes
B. no (two groups of two are connected)
C. yes

LED Astray (page 41)

Top portion showing: $73 + 19 = 92$.
Lower portion showing: $45 + 18 = 63$ or $49 + 16 = 65$.

Making Faces (page 32)

From left to right from the top: Max, Maude, Wade, Walt, Vance, Mona, Mimi, and Boris.

Mind Boggler (page 3)

The numbers ONE through TEN can be spelled by moving from letter to adjacent letter. THREE is the only number that cannot be spelled without using the same letter E two times in a row.

Mirror Images (page 11)

Figures four and seven are impossible with just one mirror.

Number Lines (page 36)

A. 35; B. 44.

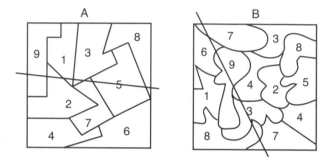

Out of Shape (page 23)

B, F, G, and I are not versions of the original shape.

Paper Clip Flip (page 5)

Number 1 is shorter than the original. Numbers 3 and 10 are longer than the original.

Paper Pinball (page 20)

10, +20, −5, +10, +15, +5, +10, −10, +15, +10, +5, +40, −20, +25, +40, −5, +10, −10, +25, +5, +15, −5, +30, −10, +15, +30, +20, + 5 = 295.

Picture This (page 39)

Pieces of Wisdom (page 29)

"To laugh often and much."

Pretzel Logic (page 34)

Pieces two and eight are not Mrs. Saline pretzels.

Ready to Roll (page 37)

Die D is not a standard die (all pairs of numbers on opposite sides should add up to seven).

Receipt Deceit (page 28)

Hank's purchases were 3.25 + 0.75 + 1.30 = 5.30 + .25 tax = $5.55. The sale before his was for 1.80 + 4.96 + 0.64 = 7.40 + .35 tax = $7.75.

Shifting Gears (page 16)

1. clockwise; 2. clockwise; 3. counterclockwise; 4. these gears won't turn.

Sketch Pad (page 38)

1. Start at the top of the three circles. Go around the first circle counterclockwise, then out across the top of the topmost bar and back across the bottom of it. Then go around the center circle counterclockwise, out across the top of the second (left-pointing) bar and back across the bottom of it. Finish by going around the bottom circle counterclockwise, out across the top of the lowest bar and back across the bottom of it. There are several variations that will work.

2. Start on the leftmost vertical line at its center point. Trace the upper left-hand square going counterclockwise. Then go three-quarters of the way around the bottom left square, also counterclockwise. Now angle down and to the right, back left, up and to the right, up and to the left, across to the right, down and to the left, across to the right, and down. Next move three-quarters of the way around the bottom right square, counterclockwise, then finish up the upper right square in a clockwise direction. Again, there are several variations.

Slice of Life (page 15)

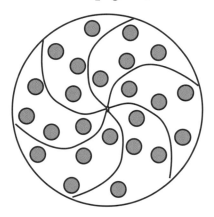

Starry Eyes (page 29)

Symbol Maze (page 27)

Starting with the circle: A1, A3, C2, A2, D3, B1, D1, B2, D2, B3, C1, and C3.

Talk for a Spell (page 25)

a-florist (FLOWERS); b-health club (WORKOUT); c-barber (HAIRCUT); d-travel agent (FLY AWAY); e-coffee shop (HOT JAVA); f-costume shop (DRESS UP); g-veterinarian (PET CARE); h-bank (SAVE NOW).

Technique-Color (page 4)

Piece A should be orange.

Ten Gold Coins (page 10)

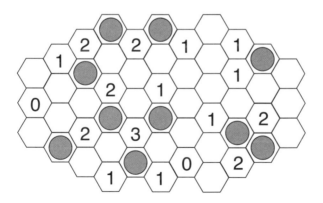

Theory of Relativity (page 5)

You are Bernie.

Three Hexes (page 9)

Numbers three and seven are made with four hexagons.

To the Letter (page 17)

In order, the letters spell "verbatim."

Tying the Knot (page 3)

She should start her subscription to *Brides* magazine. Ropes 1, 2, and 5 will form knots.

Unfolding Mystery (page 31)

1 matches a and 2 matches f.

A Whale's Tale (page 35)

The phrase is: It beats nine times per minute.

What's the Plan? (page 8)

Object one fits the plan.

Winter Eyes (page 12)

A–1; B–7; C–4.

LATERAL THINKING

The Alaskan Dream (page 72)

Scott will need to travel to a hospital in order to have the battery replaced in his pacemaker within four years.

Attorney Client Privilege (page 96)

Sam is visiting his lawyer, who had been arrested and jailed.

Brainbender #20 (page 87)

Receding hairline.

An Axe to Grind (page 75)

The tree is a Japanese bonsai variety. Two-hundred-year-old bonsai trees typically grow only a few feet in height and a few inches in diameter.

The Big Game (page 97)

The prominent citizen was the police chief. He called several of the city's most-wanted criminals, and claimed that they had won the tickets in a random drawing. When the criminals arrived to claim their tickets, they got more than they bargained for!

Bill's Birthday Surprise (page 106)

After hearing of an impending flood, Marion scrubbed her bathtub and filled it with water to be saved for drinking. Unaware that the city's water had already been shut off, Bill used the water to take a bath.

Brainbender #21 (page 89)

Unfinished Symphony.

A Bridge to Fear (page 73)

Patty was standing near one end of the bridge. She fell only a few feet to the ground.

By the Time I Get to Phoenix (page 60)

Nick knew that Frank would assume that he was referring to the West and East Coasts of America; however, he was thinking of a trip from the Atlantic Coast to the Gulf Coast of Florida. In fact, his trip took far less than the 24 hours he boasted about.

Crustacean Vacation (page 94)

As Milton launched the small boat they used to check the crab pots, he discovered a patch of dead grass where the boat had been resting. This indicated that the boat had not been moved for quite some time.

A Customs Conundrum (page 91)

Eric eventually died as a result of his skiing accident. His body was being flown home in the cargo section of a plane.

Dead Men Tell No Tales (page 60)

The man was still alive when the search party found him. He was able to tell the police the identity of his attacker. He later died at the hospital.

The Discouraging Discovery (page 78)

Vern had purchased his house for an exorbitant price with the understanding that the house had been constructed for W.C. Meadows, the famous movie star. In fact, the real estate agent had told him that W.C. Meadows had planted a sapling in the front yard when he first moved in. The storm had knocked over this very tree. While cutting up the tree, Vern counted the rings and discovered the tree was thirty years old. Unfortunately for Vern, W.C. Meadows had died forty years ago.

Brainbender #22 (page 90)

Forgive and forget.

Sweet Success (page 64)

The sugar was in the form of a cube, allowing Charlotte to pick it up by merely wetting her fingertip and touching its top.

Down on the Farm (page 85)

Jedro's farm contained large hills, which increased its total surface area by 10%.

Execution at Dawn (page 56)

When firing squads were used to carry out death sentences, a blank round was loaded into one of the guns used by the firing squad. This would allow each member of the firing squad to believe that he had not caused the prisoner's death.

Brainbender #23 (page 95)

Space Invaders.

The Expert Pilot (page 78)

The man was a Japanese kamikaze. Since he intended to crash his plane into an American battleship, he had no reason to be concerned with the faulty landing gear.

An Explosive Situation (page 102)

The man worked for a traveling circus as a human cannonball.

Express Checkout (page 106)

Barry was purchasing milk and happened to notice the picture of the boy on the carton in his shopping basket. The caption stated that it was believed the boy had been abducted by his father. The strong resemblance between the boy and the adult convinced Barry to call the authorities.

Eyes on the Prize (page 71)

Alexander's name and credit cards were being used by an impostor ever since his wallet had been stolen. As he had not filled out a raffle ticket, when his name was announced as the winner he realized that the person impersonating him must have been present and filled one out. He simply waited around for the prize to be claimed in order to discover the identity of the culprit.

Feast or Famine (page 74)

Paul was a P.O.W. While incarcerated, his captors did not abide by the Geneva Convention rules concerning the treatment of prisoners of war. Paul refused to eat after realizing that he was being fattened up for his impending release.

Brainbender #24 (page 99)

Back and forth.

A Fire Escape (page 45)

Nicole was locked in a jail cell and realized it was futile for her to attempt to leave until the guard unlocked her cell door.

First Edition (page 98)

Mr. Jones was a well-known historian, and author of several books on the subject of World War II. He and his rival, Mr. Smith, had both recently published books on the Battle of the Bulge. He knew, happily, that his book would now seem so much the better in comparison.

The Frustrated Futures Trader (page 51)

Over the weekend, Joe traded in his car for a vintage Jaguar which had its steering wheel on the right-hand side. The following Monday, he realized he would have to get out of his car every day on his way to work in order to pay the toll at the George Washington Bridge.

Hard of Darkness (page 94)

To get a tan. For Ralph, who is an albino, this is impossible.

Harry the Homeowner (page 96)

Harry had bought a doll house for his daughter. She had, of course, wasted no time in rearranging the furniture inside.

Brainbender #25 (page 103)

Weeping willow.

A Hunting Accident (page 85)

Mick is a practitioner of falconry. One of his hunting falcons was sucked into the jet's intake and caused the engine to fail.

I Bid Thee Farewell (page 83)

Dee works for a delivery service. The bid was delivered by a rival company. Taking offense to this, she discarded the bid without looking at it.

The King's Test (page 93)

The peasant left both buckets outside in freezing weather. Later that day, he took the now frozen blocks of water and milk out of the buckets, broke them into pieces and put them back into the buckets to yield an equal mixture of both.

Keep on Truckin' (page 67)

Being a truck driver himself, Lewis knew that after many hours behind the wheel, his left arm would become more tan than the other. In Australia vehicles are driven on the left-hand side of the road. Lewis saw that the truck drivers' right arms were heavily tanned and correctly surmised that they were from Australia.

The Leaky Boat (page 58)

Al intentionally sank the boat knowing this would cause the wood to swell. This would seal the cracks in the hull.

Leave It or Not (page 102)

Elizabeth had moved in a few months before. For an upcoming art show, she decided to paint a 4-pane landscape of her house year 'round. Because it was only August, and she was a novice, she felt it would help her visualize the winter scene if she removed the leaves from her ornamental trees.

Brainbender #26 (page 105)

Count Dracula.

The Long Road Ahead (page 52)

Bubba was a race car driver. Therefore he could see his destination, the finish line, at any moment during the race.

Long Time No See (page 86)

Both the women had taken a vow of silence while living in a convent. It was only later, after having left the convent, that they were allowed to speak.

Brainbender #19 (page 84)

Income tax.

The Master Mechanic (page 92)

Gary had made a wager with Shawn that he could lie in the middle of a busy highway during rush hour for ten minutes. In order to safely win the bet, Gary drove Shawn's car to a nearby highway, feigned car trouble and climbed under the GTO. Ten minutes later he emerged five hundred dollars richer!

Brainbender #18 (page 80)

On the double.

Money Troubles (page 66)

The man was charged with embezzling large sums of money. In order to post his bond he would have to use the money he had embezzled. This would have strengthened the case against him.

Monumental Achievement (page 100)

The monument the man had jumped off of was underwater. The whole town had been flooded years earlier, when a hydroelectric dam was built for a neighboring city.

Brainbender #17 (page 79)

West Indies.

More Than He Bargained For (page 50)

While window-shopping, Bert watched a news story about the grand opening of a new shopping center. Bert immediately recognized the site as the location where he had buried his accumulated wealth.

Brainbender #16 (page 77)

One foot in the grave.

Moving Day (page 82)

Herb lives on a houseboat. While moving his houseboat, Herb causes a drawbridge to be raised, thereby blocking a major road.

Brainbender #15 (page 74)

Split-second timing.

Mr. Gray's Anatomy (page 69)

Mr. Gray wants to have his head frozen once he is dead. He believes that, at some future time, technology will exist that will be able to bring the minds in frozen heads back to life.

Brainbender #14 (page 70)

Anyone for tennis?

The Mysterious Motorist (page 81)

Jennifer is a police officer. Opening the trunk partially disguises her patrol car from speeding motorists.

On the Boardwalk (page 88)

Patrick deliveries helium balloons. The helium exerts a lifting force on the cart, thereby making it more difficult to push when empty.

Out of Bounds (page 62)

The game was taking place in Cuba at the Guantánamo Bay Naval base. The ball was kicked over a fence into Cuban territory, making it dangerous to retrieve.

Brainbender #13 (page 68)

Just between you and me.

The Perfect Crime (page 104)

Rocky killed the person on the very day that an earthquake occurred. This made the person's death appear to be an accident caused by the natural disaster.

Petty Cash (page 73)

Pauline is an avid coin collector. The five antique silver dollars were appraised at one thousand dollars.

Photo Finished (page 67)

Ben had filmed his "week-long" vacation over the course of one day. On examining the tape, the police noticed that the phases of the moon did not change throughout the entire video. The moon would have changed significantly over a span of one week.

Brainbender #12 (page 64)

Bermuda Triangle.

The Pilot's Puzzle (page 101)

The pilot was flying in a war zone. He had been instructed to look for grazing animals as an indication of a safe landing area. If land mines had been present, the animals would most likely have set them off as they grazed.

Potted Plants (page 69)

An alert employee at the local power company notified the authorities that Fred was using an exorbitant amount of electricity, as compared to his previous bills. The police soon suspected that this additional power was being used for illicit purposes.

Brainbender #11 (page 63)

One step forward, two steps back.

The Prison Break (page 54)

Jim was hired by the state authorities to test the security system at a new prison. He posed as a prisoner in order to attempt an escape. When he succeeded, the authorities were embarrassed by his accomplishment.

A Reverting Development (page 98)

The storm caused a power line to be knocked down. Since the artist had been working on an ice sculpture in his refrigerated studio, he depended upon electric power to keep the work of art from melting.

Brainbender #10 (page 61)

Pin-up.

Room Despair (page 100)

The man was confined to a wheelchair. He wanted the extra room to accommodate visiting friends and relatives. The addition consisted of a second story on top of what had been a single-level home.

The Root of the Problem (page 76)

Mr. Finkel accidentally cut his neighbor's phone line while planting the tree. His neighbor suffered a heart attack and was unable to call for help.

Brainbender #6 (page 53)

Forever and ever.

The Runaway (page 65)

The man was a teammate who took a baton from Alex's hand during the course of a relay race.

The Secret Meeting (page 88)

Their intimate conversations take place in a confessional. Therefore neither one can clearly see the other's face.

A Sense of Direction (page 81)

B.J. was the architect who had designed the building. Knowing the layout of the building, she easily found her way to her destination.

Brainbender #9 (page 59)

At the point of no return.

Shed Some Light (page 83)

The hermit's house was powered by photo-electric solar cells, which only operated in direct sunlight.

A Shooting at Midnight (page 56)

The man shot his rooster, which had awakened him with its crowing every morning for the past ten years. Since he had recently retired, there was no longer any reason to be awakened at such an early hour.

Shore Sighted (page 104)

The stranded group sets off flares in the hope that those seeing them would come to their rescue. Unfortunately, the boat trip took place on a holiday, part of the reason for the outing, and the onlookers seeing the flares assumed that they were simply part of the firework displays that were part of the holiday celebrations.

Shortchanged (page 65)

Minnie was traveling in Mexico when she received the tip. Unfortunately, all of the change she had in her pocket was still American currency. Minnie could not find anyone to exchange her money.

The Sky Diver (page 71)

Unfortunately for Pierre, he did not survive the jump. However, his brother was in need of a transplant and was blessed enough to receive the necessary organ from an ideal donor.

The Sky's the Limit (page 76)

The treasure map relied on celestial navigation. Therefore Henry needed to wait until a specific date for a constellation to appear in the sky.

Swimming with the Fishes (page 62)

The man was ice fishing on a frozen lake. Unable to find the hole through which he had fallen, he consequently drowned.

Brainbender #8 (page 57)

Mixed bag.

Temporary Housing (page 90)

Jake had built a large tree house, which surrounded the main trunk. When the tree grows in diameter, the framing of the tree house will gradually be destroyed.

Theft in a Pub (page 48)

J.P. was a counterfeiter. He left the wallet in plain view, knowing it was likely to be stolen, and the money spent. He then watched the transaction, thereby learning if the bogus money would pass as real currency without having to take the risk himself.

Brainbender #7 (page 55)

Bend over backwards.

To Tell a Mockingbird (page 48)

Christopher was a priest. In the confessional at church, John told the priest about his involvement in the crime. Christopher later learned of Bob's role while attending a church bake sale. Catholic priests are constrained from revealing information imparted to them in a confessional.

Brainbender #5 (page 51)

Ambiguous.

The Unsuccessful Suicide (page 46)

The building was on fire at the same time the man tried to commit suicide, leading the police to believe he was only trying to save himself from the fire.

Brainbender #4 (page 50)

Round of drinks on the house.

An Untimely Death (page 52)

Cal was a coal miner and his pet, Roscoe, was a canary. In a bygone era, canaries were sometimes used to alert miners to the presence of flammable gases accumulating in the mines, which could cause a disastrous explosion. The small birds' low tolerance for gases would cause them to die, thereby warning the miners of the danger.

Brainbender #3 (page 49)

No U-Turn.

What's It All About? (page 80)

Mack is a champion featherweight boxer. After his binge he was unable to make weight for his title bout.

Brainbender #2 (page 47)

Square meal.

Whose Vault Is It? (page 87)

Using bubble gum, the thief disguised himself by blowing a large bubble, thereby concealing his face from the camera.

Wonder Woman (page 58)

The woman was an astronaut aboard the Space Shuttle. In zero gravity conditions, large heavy objects can be easily manipulated.

Brainbender #1 (page 46)

Red in the face.

Wood That I Could (page 54)

Tom was expecting a boat to pass by the island on the tenth night. Since he had only enough wood for one fire, Tom waited until the boat was in sight. Coincidentally, this was the same night that it began to rain.

The Yard Sale (page 91)

Gerald is blind and fears he would be shortchanged by the purchaser. The bank teller would insure the proper amount is paid.

GEOMETRICAL
GYRATIONS

Cutting Cloth (page 111)

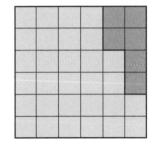

The Military Band (page 112)

Let's suppose the band was originally in the form of a square and that the number of musicians was n^2. If it was possible for the musicians to change their formation to that of a rectangle with $n + 5$ columns, that means that $n + 5$ divides n^2. Since $n^2 = (n + 5)(n - 5) + 25$, this means that $n + 5$ divides 25. The only divisor of 25 greater than 5 is 25 itself, so $n + 5 = 25$ and $n = 20$. The number of musicians in the band was, therefore, 400.

Arthur's Will (page 121)

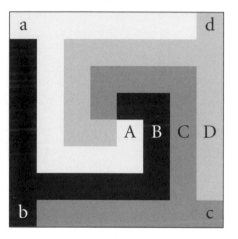

Three Partitions (page 118)

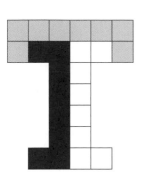

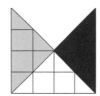

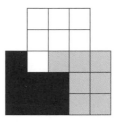

Change of Flag (page 115)

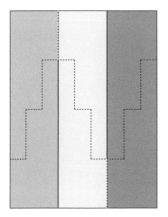

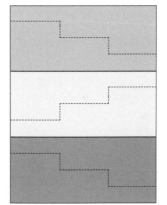

A Question of Space (page 113)

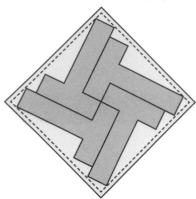

The Jealous Boyfriends (page 117)

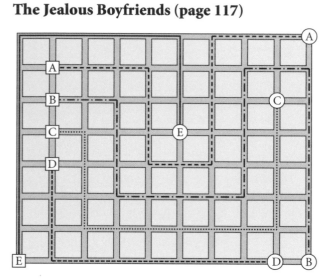

A Spiral of Matches (page 119)

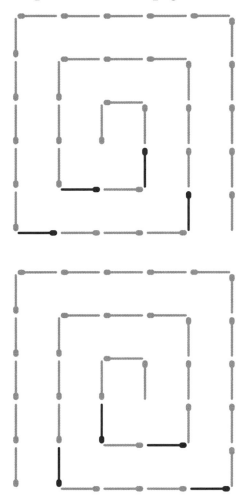

Triangle Salad (page 114)

The number of triangles is 78.

Two Sheets of Paper (page 120)

The covered portion of the sheet is greater than the uncovered portion. To convince yourself of this, notice how in the figure all of the uncovered part of the sheet corresponds to the two triangles that make up only part of the portion of the sheet that is covered.

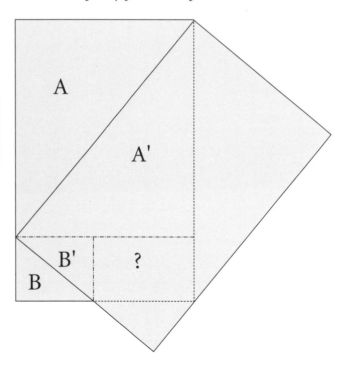

Two Circles and a Rectangle (page 116)

Shown below is the way to draw two circles and a rectangle in such a way that the three shapes intersect 18 times.

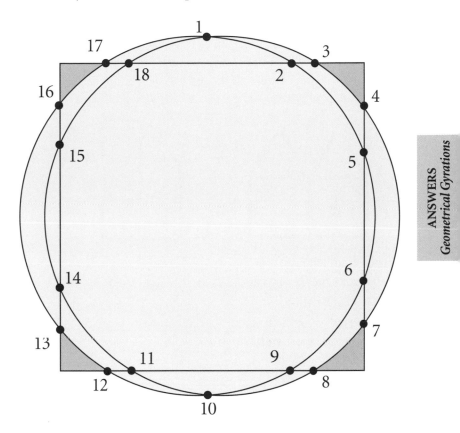

Fit to Be Tiled (page 124)

The 8 × 8 table can be covered with shape B (but not shape A).
The 8 × 6 table can be covered with shape A (but not shape B).

Match Boxes (page 123)

Only piece e will not form a box.

Stick Houses (page 123)

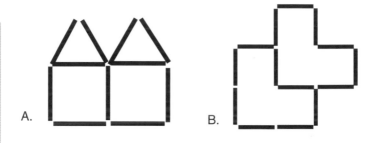

A.   B.

Thirteen Candles (page 122)

The candles form 50 triangles: 18 made by the six points around
the edge; 18 using the full side of the two large triangles; 12 made
of half of a full side; and 2 large triangles.

Flat Tire (page 127)

Let the radii of the larger and smaller circles be R and r respectively. The desired area is then $\pi R^2 - \pi r^2 = \pi(R^2 - r^2)$.

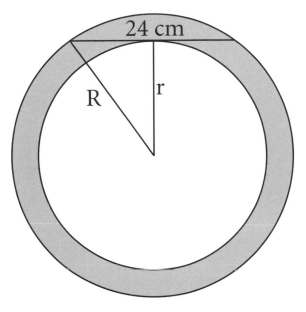

Using the Pythagorean theorem, it can be seen that $R^2 - r^2 = (24/2)^2 = 144$, so the desired arca is $144\pi - 452.4$ sq. cm.

Shot Through the Heart (page 125)

To show the perimeter is divided into two equal lengths, whatever the angle of the arrow, let the diameter of each of the smaller semicircles (and thus the radius of the large semicircle) be d and let the arrow lie at an angle of a radians to the horizontal.

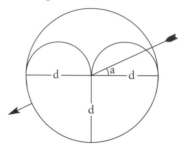

The perimeter length lying above the horizontal line is $\pi d/2 + \pi d/2 = \pi d$, which is the perimeter length lying below the horizontal line. Therefore, to prove the heart's perimeter is divided into two equal lengths, we need to show that the part of the perimeter above the horizontal line and below the arrow is equal in length to the part of the perimeter that is below the horizontal line and above the arrow.

Begin by letting C be the center of the smaller semicircle on the right as shown below:

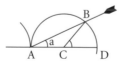

Since triangle ABC is isosceles, angle BCD is 2a radians. Thus the length of arc BD is $\frac{2a}{2\pi}$ multiplied by the perimeter of the small circle = $\frac{2a}{2\pi} \times \pi d$ = ad. This is also the length of the arc of the big semicircle that is below the horizontal line and above the arrow and so the result is proven.

Unhinged (page 130)

Construct the line CG as shown below:

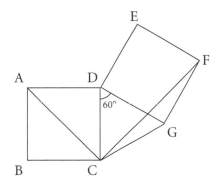

Since DC = DG and angle CDG is 60°, triangle CDG is equilateral, so DC = DG = CG.

Thus, triangle CGF is isosceles, since CG = GF. Angle CGF is angle CGD + angle DGF, which is 60° + 90°, or 150°. So angles GCF and GFC are both 15°.

Since angle DCG is 60° and angle GCF is 15°, angle FCD is 45°. Angle ACD is also 45°, so angle ACF is the sum of FCD and ACD, or 45° + 45°, which is 90°.

Twinkle, Twinkle (page 129)

Let the width of the star be 2a, and construct a line from the center of the star (and circle) to where one of the two outer threads meets the circle.

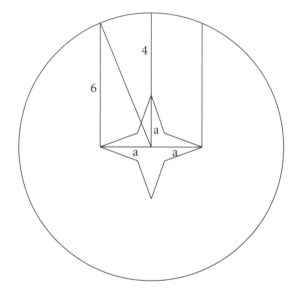

Clearly, the radius of the circle is 4 + a. The diagonal line is a radius, but it is also the hypotenuse of a right-angled triangle with sides of length 6 and a. Thus by the Pythagorean theorem we have $6^2 + a^2 = (4 + a)^2$, so a equals 2.5 cm and the width of the star is 5 cm.

Go Fish (page 131)

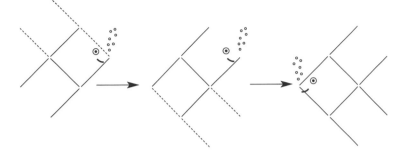

Quilting Bee (page 126)

To prove this, color the large triangle of 36 units in area as shown, giving 21 light and 15 dark unit triangles.

If the twelve available shapes are colored in a similar manner, ten are found to have an equal number of light and dark unit triangles. In the remaining two cases, there are four light and two dark (or vice versa). However, to tile the shape above requires at least three pieces where the difference between the numbers of light and dark triangles is two. Since there are only two such pieces, no solution is possible.

Back to Basics (page 128)

The base n of the measurements can be found using the Pythagorean theorem, which gives the following decimal equation: $7^2 + (2n)^2 = (n + 3)^2 + (n + 8)^2$, from which $n = 12$. Thus the base being used in the question is 12, and using this base, the hypotenuse measures 21. In base ten the sides are 7, 24, and 25, and 15, 20, and 25.

WORDS, WORDS, WORDS

Vowel Exchange (page 135)

1. BET BUT
2. SCRAP SCRIP
3. SHIP SHOP
4. STRONG STRING
5. MAST MUST
6. LOVE LIVE
7. CHIP CHOP
8. QUICK QUACK
9. PORT PART
10. HIRE HERE
11. DOG DIG
12. ORE ARE
13. GRIPE GROPE
14. DEPARTMENT DEPORTMENT

15. BLAND BLEND or GRAND GRIND
16. SPIKE SPOKE
17. BARN BURN
18. AND END
19. WITCH WATCH
20. WELL WILL

Rhyme Time (page 137)

1. factor actor tractor
2. session expression aggression
3. reckoned fecund second
4. dome home Rome loam
5. belief grief brief
6. Sean (Shawn) fawn lawn dawn
7. Othello mellow fellow
8. Who knew you flew?
9. goose moose loose
10. Perot go slow
11. Tonto Toronto pronto
12. poker smoker joker
13. believer retriever fever
14. sukiyaki rocky hockey

15. majority seniority authority
16. acquittal whittle little
17. topic myopic Tropic
18. utter putter sputter
19. fat cat sat at Bat
20. hilly silly billy

Broadway Shows (page 139)

1. *The Most Happy Fella*
2. *Kiss Me, Kate*
3. *Grease*
4. *A Chorus Line*
5. *The King and I*
6. *Good News*
7. *Woman of the Year*
8. *Cabaret*
9. *Damn Yankees*
10. *Pajama Game*

Broadway Songs (page 140)

1. "Climb Every Mountain"
2. "Thank Heaven for Little Girls"

3. "If I Were a Rich Man"

4. "The Impossible Dream"

5. "You'll Never Walk Alone"

6. "I Could Have Danced All Night"

7. "Luck, Be a Lady"

8. "There's a Place for Us"

9. "People Will Say We're in Love"

10. "Memory"

Buried Song Titles (page 141)

1. eneMY hideaWAY

2. cOLD unMANageable dRIVERs

3. conDOminium compREhension comMIssion

4. foreCLOSEd phoTOgenic baYOU

5. vALLEY vaCATion

6. airBORNe aTOms encumBEr WILDerness

7. sTEAl comFORtable flaTWOrms

8. cLOVEs suppleMEnt wisDOm

9. weaTHEr's moROSE

10. poiSOnous cuRARE

Call Letters (page 142)

1. CUBS, CAMP, or KNOT
2. KENT
3. WISH
4. WXYZ, CODA, or WRAP
5. XRAY
6. COLD
7. KING
8. CLAM or CORN
9. CRAM
10. KANE

Hangwords (page 143)

1. GARBAGE
2. OBNOXIOUS
3. QUACKERY or QUIRKILY
4. MYRRH
5. FLASHLIGHT
6. EXQUISITE
7. GHERKIN
8. CONCOCTION
9. UBIQUITOUS
10. INVOLVEMENT *or* DEVOLVEMENT

Common Interiors (page 144)

1. cUTLAS and oUTLASt
2. cRAVEn and gRAVEl
3. oCTEt and aCTEd
4. jOCKEy and rOCKEd
5. cLIMb and bLIMp
6. eACh and bACk
7. aLIEn and fLIEr
8. cANOe and mANOr
9. gIANt and pIANo
10. pHASe and cHASm

Repeaters (page 145)

1. CUCUMBER *or* ALFALFA
2. EERIE, SUSURROUS, *or* ULULATING
3. VIVID
4. PAPAL
5. BARBARIAN
6. TATAMI
7. PAPAYA
8. OOLONG
9. TINTINNABULATORS

10. NONOCCURRENCE
11. COCOA
12. REREAD
13. OOZED
14. LILIES
15. MIMIC
16. EELS
17. COCOON
18. LLAMA
19. OODLES
20. COCONUT

Crazy Z (page 147)

1. pizza, freezer
2. blitz, zone
3. zip, zero
4. lazy, zoo
5. zap, dozen
6. Fitzgerald, Zachary
7. Hazel, dozed
8. ooze, hazard
9. Brazil, Mozambique
10 hazy, gaze

Food Words (page 148)

1. cantaloupe (can't elope)
2. anise (a niece)
3. salad (Sal add)
4. cutlet (cut let)
5. pastry (pace, tree)
6. kielbasa (kill Bossa)
7. pumpernickel (pump a nickel)
8. rosemary (rose Mary)
9. fowl (foul)
10. ginger (Ginger)
11. mango (man go)
12. berry (bury)
13. turmeric (term, Erik)
14. lentil (Lent til)
15. salmon (Sam on)
16. pizza (Pete's a)
17. nutmeg (nut, Meg)
18. bacon (bake in)
19. yogurt ("Yo, Gert!")
20. mutton (Mutt &)

Automotive Words (page 150)

1. dashboard (dash bored)
2. Mustang (must Tang)
3. valves
4. Nissan (Nice on)
5. convertible (convert a bull) or driveable (drive a bull)
6. Landau (land Dow)
7. Fleetwood (fleet would)
8. gearshift (Gere shift)
9. showroom (show room)
10. motel (Moe tell)
11. Dodge (dodge)
12. brakes (breaks)
13. Pontiac (Ponti yak)
14. highway (high way)
15. steering (steer wring)
16. traction (track shun)
17. Goodyear (good year)
18. Tercel (terse sell)
19. Catera (cat tear a)
20. Saab (sob) or travel, road, or crank

Computer Talk (page 152)

1. motherboard (mother bored)
2. zip (zip) or run (run)
3. website (Webb's sight)
4. network (net work) or netcast (net cast)
5. RAM (ram)
6. icon (Ike on)
7. Fortran (fort ran)
8. Java (Java)
9. Intel (in Tel)
10. gigabyte (gig, a bite or jig, a bite) or byte (bite)
11. Chip (chip)
12. floppy (flop Pee)
13. drive (drive) or drag (drag)
14. Gateway (gate weigh)
15. upgrade (up grade)
16. format (for Matt)
17. Intuit (into it)
18. Spam (spam)
19. Excel (XL)
20. Lotus (Lo, 'tis)

World Capitals (page 154)

1. Berlin (Berle in)
2. Papeete (Papa eighty)
3. Seoul (sole)
4. Canberra (Can Berra)
5. Havana (Have Anna)
6. Taipei (tie pay)
7. Stockholm (stock home)
8. Lisbon (Liz been)
9. Baghdad (bag Dad)
10. Amman (om on)
11. Washington (washing ton)
12. Monrovia (Monroe via)
13. Tripoli (triple E)
14. Rome (roam)
15. Bucharest (book, arrest)
16. Sofia (Sophie a)
17. Manila (manila)
18. Ankara (anchor a)
19. Warsaw (War saw)
20. Beirut (bay, root)

Name Games (page 156)

1. Mike, mike

2. Carol, carol

3. Rose, rose

4. Don, don

5. Tad, tad

6. Bo, Bow

7. Al, al.

8. Bill, Bill

9. Art, art

10. Sue, sue

Reversible Words (page 158)

1 Ma, am

This sentence is a palindrome: It reads the same backward and forward.

2. pot, top

3. It, ti

4. mad, dam

5. sub, bus

6. pets, step

7. sleep, peels

8. star, rats

9. dab, bad

10. saw, was

11. Oh, Ho

12. smart, trams

13. part, trap

14. gum, mug

15. may, yam

16. slap, pals

17. stink, knits

18. pal, lap

19. are, era

20. ten, net

21. edit, tide

22. mood, doom

23. pan, nap

24. evil, live

25. reviled, deliver

26. gas, sag

27. not, ton

28. won, now

29. parts, strap

30. stun, nuts

31. stop, pots

32. laced, decal

33. swap, paws

34. tip, pit

35. tub, but

36. emit, time

37. tap, pat

38. bat, tab

39. pools, sloop

40. laud, dual

Cities & States (page 161)

1. Montgomery

2. Selma (sell Ma)

3. Nome (nom)

4. Danbury (Dan bury)

5. Dover (Dover)

6. Jonesboro (Jones burrow)

7. Nogales (no gal is)

8. Buckeye (buck I)

9. Carmel (car Mel)

10. Bakersfield (Baker's field)

11. Boulder (bolder)

12. Limon (lime on)

13. Norwalk (nor walk)

14. Juneau (June know)

15. Hope (hope)

16. Lewes (lose)

17. Pensacola (pens a cola)

18. Sebring (Sea bring)

19. Macon (makin')

20. Augusta (August a)

21. Waimea (Why may a)

22. Waikiki (why Kiki)

23. Boise (boy's E)

24. Nampa ('Nam Pa)

25. Moline (Moe lean)

26. Champaign (Champagne)

27. Marion (marry in)

28. Gary (Garry)

29. Ames (aims)

30. Davenport (davenport)

31. Topeka (to peek a)

32. Liberal (liberal)

33. Ashland (ash land)

34. Florence (Florence)

35. Hammond (ham and)

36. Monroe (Monroe)

37. Bangor (bang or)

38. Orono (or Ono)

39. Annapolis (an apple is)

40. Westmore (west more)

41. Amherst (am Hearst)

42. Andover (and over)

43. Wayne (Wayne)

44. Dearborn (deer born)

45. Rochester (Rochester)

46. Mankato (man Kato)

47. Greenwood (green would)

48. Jackson (jacks in)

49. Joplin (Joplin)

50. Independence (in dependents')

51. Helena (Helen a)

52. Billings (billings)

53. Lincoln (link in)

54. Kearney (care knee)

55. Ely (E. Lee)

56. Henderson (Henderson)

57. Manchester (man Chester)

58. Concord (Concord)

59. Trenton (Trent in)

60. Newark (new ark)

61. Raton (rat on)

62. Gallup (Gallup)

63. Albany (all Benny)

64. Utica (you tick a)

65. Charlotte (Charlotte)

66. Hatteras (Hatter is)

67. Bismarck (biz mark)

68. Fargo (Favre go)

69. Dayton (date in)

70. Canton (cant in)

71. Sallisaw (Sally saw)

72. Ada (aid a)

73. Portland (port land)

74. Bend (bend)

75. Hershey (her she)

76. Easton (east in)

77. Newport (new port)

78. Kingston (Kingston)

79. Columbia (column be a)

80. Conway (con weigh)

81. Pierre (pear)

82. Mitchell (Mitchell)

83. Kingsport (king's sport)

84. Bristol (Bristol)

85. Tyler (tile or)

86. Austin (Austin)

87. Vernal (vernal)

88. Ogden (Ogden)

89. Rutland (rut land)

90. Stowe (stow)

91. Fairfax (fair fax)

92. Reston (rest in)

93. Tacoma (to comb a)

94. Spokane (spoke an)

95. Wheeling (wheeling)

96. Huntington (hunting tin)

97. Kenosha (can OSHA)

98. Madison (Madison)

99. Sundance (son dance)

100. Laramie (Lara, me)

IT'S LOGICAL

Alligator Ally (page 177)

The alligator is on the left and is lying.

Calendar Girls (page 180)

The only day that works for everyone is Friday the 24th.

Categorically Speaking (page 174)

	S	C	A	M	P
Girls' names:	Scarlet	Candy	Amber	Myrtle	Pearl
Colors:	sand	coral	amethyst	magenta	purple
Trees:	spruce	chestnut	apple	mango	palm
Flowers:	snowball	camellia	amaryllis	magnolia	primrose
On a beach:	shell	chair	anemone	mussel	pail

The Chips Are Down (page 184)

Clock Wise (page 187)

It is 9:45.

Concentration (page 179)

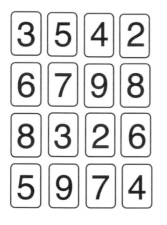

Detective Story (page 174)

Slooth should arrest the man in the Civic. Chiller is calling from Thunder Bay, Ontario, where they measure the temperature in Celsius. Thirty degrees Celsius is 86 degrees Fahrenheit.

Fit for a Princess (page 176)

The princess can wear four combinations of one piece of jewelry, six combinations of two, four combinations of three, and one combination of all four jewels, for a total of 15 different combinations.

Get the Scoop (page 175)

The free ice cream will be on the first Tuesday in July.

Guesstimation (page 182)

1-f; 2-e; 3-a; 4-g; 5-c; 6-b; 7-d.

It Takes All Sorts (page 183)

Kevin likes bananas. He likes words that alternate vowels and consonants, like his name. Rhonda uses a comb. She likes words that have silent letters, like her name.

Losing Track (page 173)

Deb cheated. The answers are: 1. bison; 2. caribou; 3. deer; 4. moose; 5. mountain goat.

Orchestration (page 178)

Two violinists are fencers (they are also in the snake club). Two cellists are in neither group.

Order, Please (page 182)

In the first case, the kids are in order of the length of their first names; in the second, the names form a chain in which the last letter of each name is the first letter of the next.

Phone-y Words (page 185)

Across: ugly, food, band, liar.
Down: teak, inch, knob, weep.

Pie-Eyed (page 178)

Here's one answer: Put five cherries in one bowl, five cherries in another, and put one of those inside the third bowl, which holds two cherries.

The Right Direction (page 181)

Wendy was looking at the scrap of paper upside down. They should have been looking for 819 Pooh. Ray recognized that Owl Street and Rabbit Court were part of the same Winnie-the-Pooh themed neighborhood.

Ruff and Ready (page 177)

There were 28 people and 35 dogs.

Seeds of Doubt (page 186)

The potatoes are in squares C1 and D1.

Whoa, Baby! (page 183)

Caroline was born on a Tuesday. She was 18 months old when her "birthday" fell on a Tuesday for the third time (in her second July).

Three Cards (page 188)

The three cards placed on the table are the king of spades, the queen of spades, and the queen of hearts.

The False Coin (page 199)

To work out which is the false coin you must proceed as follows:

1. The eighteen coins are divided into three groups of 6. Two of these groups are weighed against each other. This enables you to determine which of the three groups contains the false coin.

2. The group of 6 coins that contains the false coin is divided into three pairs of coins, and two of these pairs are weighed against one another. This allows you to determine which pair contains the false coin.

3. Finally, the two coins belonging to the pair known to contain the false coin are weighed against one another. The lighter is the false coin.

Much more difficult is the problem of how to detect a false coin from among twelve identical coins when the only thing identifiable about the false coin from the others is that it has a different weight and you don't know if it's heavier or lighter than the others. This operation too can be carried out using a set of scales just three times, but it requires a considerably more complicated strategy.

True or False (page 188)

All the statements, except the ninth, are false.

The Football Fans (page 195)

If the two teams are A and B and you are a supporter of team A and you don't want any of your fellow supporters to end up walking to the stadium, organize them in a circle starting at the point where the driver starts and reading clockwise as follows: A, A, A, A, B, B, B, B, B, A, A, B, A, A, A, B, A, B, B, A, A, B, B, B, A, B, B, A, A, B.

The Portrait of an Unknown Man (page 196)

The gentleman in the portrait is the son of the man who is speaking.

The Drama Festival (page 197)

The festival lasted at least six days.

Let the 11 groups be A1, A2, A3, ... A11. If the 11 groups put on their plays according to the following program of events, it is easy to see how each group was able to attend at least one of the performances of every other group.

Group	Days on which they performed
A1	1 and 2
A2	1 and 3
A3	1 and 4
A4	1 and 5
A5	2 and 3
A6	2 and 4
A7	2 and 5
A8	3 and 4
A9	3 and 5
A10	4 and 5
A11	6

It can be shown that a similar program of events allowing each group to attend at least one of all the other groups' performances would not have been possible in five days.

Athletes' Tales (page 193)

The winner was Bea, and Carol was lying. With only Carol lying, Ann, Carol, and Dorothy couldn't have won. All other possibilities don't work in one way or another.

The Cycle Race (page 189)

"Crazy" Charles was runner-up in the race because in each of the 14 stages he beat 7 different competitors, and he beat them by more time than the accumulated time that they beat him by in all the other stages of the tour. Since 7 × 14 = 98, there was only one cyclist that he never beat and that was the champion.

The Incomplete Grid (page 192)

Three Thorny Matters (page 190)

- You shouldn't bet. To win the bet you must first pay out five hundred dollars, but you will only get back one hundred dollars if you do indeed win. And it is hardly likely that someone is going to give you a thousand dollars in exchange for five hundred and thereby lose the bet. So, don't bet.

- One of the mistakes is in the spelling of "sentence": the second "s" should be a "c." The other mistake is that there is only one mistake!

- The amount of wine in the water glass is the same as the amount of water in the wine glass.

Two Mistaken Students (page 198)

The number the teacher wrote was 25,740.

Let N be the number we are looking for. Since all the students, except two who spoke one after the other, were correct, it can be deduced that N can be divided by 1, 2, 3, 4, 5, 6, 10, 11, 12, and 13. This is because if 2 does not divide N, neither does 4; if 3 does not divide N, neither does 6; if 5 does not divide N, neither does 10; and so on. All of this leaves 7, 8, and 9 as the only possible numbers that do not divide N. It is therefore necessary to examine two cases:

Case 1. N is not divisible by 8 and 9. In this case, however, the smallest number divisible by all the other numbers up to 13 (i.e., their least common multiple) is 60,060, a number greater than the one written on the blackboard by the teacher.

Case 2. N is not divisible by 7 and 8. The least common multiple of the remaining numbers is 25,740, and since any other multiple of the same numbers is greater than 50,000, this must have been the number written by the teacher.

Three Sisters (page 191)

The sister's ages are 2, 2, and 9.

Since the product of the ages of the three sisters is 36, the sisters' ages will be one of the following sets of three numbers: (1, 1, 36); (1, 2, 18); (1, 3, 12); (1, 4, 9); (1, 6, 6); (2, 2, 9); (2, 3, 6); and (3, 3, 4). These sets of numbers add up, respectively, to 38, 21, 16, 14, 13, 13, 11, and 10. Since Fred knows the age of his own oldest son, with this information he could have worked out the ages of the three sisters unless the oldest son were 13, in which case their ages could have been either (1, 6, 6) or (2, 2, 9). The final piece of information provided by his friend enables Fred to conclude that the sisters' ages are 2, 2, and 9.

The Ball (page 194)

Maurice took Serge's coat and Phil's hat while Phil took John's coat and Serge's hat.

INDEX

━━━━━━